COMBAT AND SURVIVAL

WHAT IT TAKES TO FIGHT AND WIN

VOLUME
4

Originally published in the United Kingdom in weekly parts **COMBAT & SURVIVAL** is a study of the armed forces at work. It shows the skills taught to soldiers and the way in which military units operate. It examines the weapons and equipment used by different armies; and, by looking at recruit training and exercises, **COMBAT & SURVIVAL** demonstrates how the armed forces develop individual responsibility, leadership and initiative.

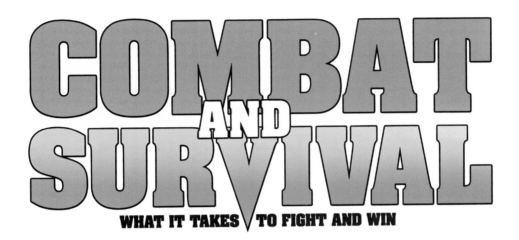

COMBAT AND SURVIVAL

WHAT IT TAKES TO FIGHT AND WIN

VOLUME
4

H. S. STUTTMAN, INC. *publishers*   Westport, Connecticut 06889

Contents
Volume 4

Published by H. S. STUTTMAN INC.
Westport, Connecticut 06889
© Aerospace Publishing 1991
ISBN 0-87475-560-3

Combat Skills

BEATING THE CLIMATE

The landing was easy. They had complete air superiority, and the AH-64s and A-10s were making sure that nothing on the ground was sticking its head up too far. Schultz rode down onto the beach out of the hold of the amphibious assault ship, and directed the APC up the scrub-covered dune. At the top he stopped. Stretching away in front of him was – nothing.

Completely empty country. Dull brown and grey. Not a sign of anything green or growing. Not a sign of movement. Yet he knew there must be at least ten thousand men out there. This, he thought, was going to be a hell of a place to fight a war.

5 TIPS FOR DESERT WARFARE

1. You need about two weeks to become acclimatised to high temperatures, with progressive degrees of heat exposure and exertion.
2. Keep fully clothed, but wear loose garments; this reduces your sweat loss.
3. The power of the sun is not reduced by clouds, so do not expose your skin simply because it has clouded over.
4. Wear a scarf or triangular bandage around your neck and use it to protect your face and neck against the sun and sand.
5. Drink small quantities of water often, rather than large amounts occasionally.

Desert warfare is tank warfare: flat terrain allows direct fire weapons to be used to their maximum range and mechanised units to make the most of their superior mobility.

R76327

It is essential to protect your eyes from the dust and bright light; unacclimatised troops can easily suffer from impaired vision. Tank crew have a problem with their clothing, which needs to be cool but flame-resistant.

But in many ways the desert is the easiest place to fight. No towns and cities to take, no civilians to jam the roads trying to escape the fighting. But it can be more forbidding than even the Arctic: the temperature differential from night to day can be a hundred and fifty degrees. In places there's no water to be found for hundreds of miles.

Learning to cope

Yet the soldier has to learn to take the hard desert life in his stride. The job, as always, is to get into action, overwhelm the enemy forces, and win the battle. The hardest part of your training is learning to cope with living conditions that would make other people give up. And learning to cope so well that they don't affect your ability to do your job.

In desert conditions there's no real substitute for acclimatisation. It won't give you total protection, but a two-week period with progressively longer periods spent exposed to the conditions and a programme of increasing physical exertion will go a long way towards safeguarding your health.

In these days of rapid deployment,

Camels can lose 30 per cent of their body weight without problems: this is fatal to humans. Here, a Chadian camel caravan plods towards the front during the fighting with Libya, April 1987.

too. Remember that sand-blasting is used to clean metal parts of dirt and rust: that's what the desert wind will do to your skin unless you keep yourself covered up. In severe sandstorms, visibility can drop to nil. Don't wander away from your unit unless there are safety lines rigged to lead you back to the base area.

Salt, water and dehydration

Seventy-five per cent of your body weight is water. Lose just two and a half per cent and your performance and stamina will be down by at least a quarter. Lose 15 per cent and you'll never have to worry about anything ever again. Because water is scarce in the desert, basic water discipline is essential. The rule is "little and often".

Each individual carries enough water to last to the next re-supply, with a small margin for emergencies, but men doing heavy labour in shade temperatures may need as much as 24

that may not be possible. Where troops have to be pitched into desert conditions and go to work immediately, as much activity as possible should take place in the cooler hours.

Sun, wind, sand and dust

The worst natural enemies in the desert are the sun, the wind and the sand, and dust. The sun attacks in two ways: it burns, and it causes the body to overheat.

A deep tan is the best protection against sunburn, but don't try to do too much too soon. Expose yourself to the sun in the early morning and late afternoon to start with, and take it in

small doses: five minutes on the first day, increasing gradually.

That may sound too conservative, but the power of desert sun can't be overstated – and once you've overdone it, that's it. Don't forget that the sun is as dangerous on cloudy days as it is when the sky is clear. Use a protective cream but don't rely on it. Remember – overexposure to the sun can kill you.

The wind is completely free of moisture in the desert. It will dry your skin, eyes and mouth. The only protection is to keep yourself covered, even though the heat may be unbearable. Once again, better uncomfortable than dead. Vehicle crews should always wear goggles and some sort of scarf. Use lip salve and skin creams to keep the exposed areas moist.

The wind whips up sand and dust,

Above: Paratroopers from the 82nd Airborne Division on exercise in Egypt wear the new US Army desert camouflage kit: note the bandana and tinted goggles.

Left: Once you are acclimatised you can develop an ability for 'pre-drinking': consuming more water than you want before exposure to heat and exertion.

These US Marines are ready to go ashore on the coast of the Sinai desert as US forces train for desert warfare in readiness for American intervention in the Middle East.

pints per day, and quantities like that can only be carried in bulk. If the water ration doesn't come up to requirements, then there's no alternative but to reduce the amount of work you do.

In high desert temperatures, where the humidity in the atmosphere is zero, even a resting man can lose as much as a pint of water an hour through perspiration. Four hours without replenishment and you're dangerously close to the two and a half per cent loss level.

You sweat to cool the body down. Retain the sweat on the skin and you improve the efficiency of the cooling process. Never remove clothing. If possible, damp clothing down with water that's unsuitable for drinking. Impure water can also be used for washing, vehicle radiators and the like.

Thirst isn't an adequate warning of dehydration, so you must watch out for other signs such as darker-than-usual urine. Surprisingly, some people are reluctant to drink their full ration. A variety of fruit flavourings are provided in US Army ration packs to make sometimes unpleasant water better-tasting and more attractive.

Apart from water, when you sweat you lose salt, and that can be fatal as well. Issue rations have sufficient salt for a man drinking up to eight pints of water a day, but if your consumption is higher then you must supplement the salt intake too. When salt tablets are issued, don't eat them, but dissolve them in water and take them that way.

Clothing

For the infantryman, lightweight shirts and combat pants – light in colour, not the usual green of combat fatigues – are suitable, but tank and artillery crews always have a problem with clothing. It has to be light enough not to overheat them, but still give good protection from burns. Happily, new materials are available that do the job competently.

Lightweight jungle boots are unsuitable; the sand will fill them as soon as you can empty them out, and sharp stones and rocks will cut them to pieces. Strong, high-leg combat boots with a folded tongue are the only things worth having, and even then

EFFECTS OF LIGHT IN THE DESERT

The powerful sun and low cloud density combine to produce unusually bright and glaring light conditions during the day. In certain circumstances, light allows such unlimited visibility that it is easy to grossly underestimate distances.

By contrast, visibility can often be reduced by mirages or heat shimmer when heated air rises from the extremely hot desert. This effect is made worse when you are looking into the sun or using magnifying optical instruments such as binoculars. Because mirages distort the shape of objects, observation is best at dawn and dusk when the air is cooler.

Soviet T-72 tank in close-up

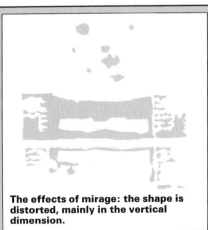

The effects of mirage: the shape is distorted, mainly in the vertical dimension.

Combat Skills

GO FOR THE HIGH GROUND

In desert warfare, high ground is critically important because otherwise your view is obstructed by the dust thrown up by moving vehicles. Also, if you are high enough above the desert floor, the worst effects of heat shimmer and mirage can be avoided. If he knows his business, the enemy will attack you when the sun is low and behind him. If you are at ground level you will be badly dazzled, so go for the high ground.

All glass, from vehicle windscreens to telescopic and night sights, will deteriorate very quickly if exposed to blown sand. Keep all glass and plastic covered when not in use.

Temperature variation from night to day causes the air and all liquids to expand and contract violently. Servicing a vehicle in the heat of the day will often produce under-inflated tyres and under-filled fuel and oil tanks after nightfall. Check the vehicles immediately before going into combat, and take whatever action is necessary to bring them up to operating specification.

Movement to contact

Because of the climate, the terrain and the distances involved in open country, it's impossible to travel any distance on foot. This puts a heavy load on those responsible for the vehicles, and on the supply routes, too.

they won't last if you don't look after them. A non-greasy dressing such as saddle soap will keep them from cracking. Use it on the soles as well as the uppers.

Care of equipment

The climate and the dusty, sandy environment make it essential to pay a lot of attention to care and maintenance even of simple kit. Clean weapons much more frequently than in normal conditions, and never allow oil and grease to build up. Use the minimum amount of lubrication on moving parts. Keep the muzzle and ejection opening of the rifle covered, and cover other, heavier weapons completely when they're not in use.

Always use a filter when re-fuelling vehicles, and pay attention to air filters, too. Diesel engines are particularly vulnerable to dust in their air supply. Inline fuel filters and oil filters should be cleaned or changed more often than normal.

An Israeli tank commander's view during the fighting in the Sinai desert, October 1973. Even in this open terrain many tank engagements took place at ranges of 1500 metres and less.

The desert is empty; you can't rely on finding supplies of even the most common items (the shortage of water is only one example), and so re-supply and combat support, combined with the principle of carrying with you everything you could possibly need, is more important than in any other theatre of operations.

Using the terrain

The chief characteristic of every type of desert is the complete absence of ground-covering vegetation. The infantryman often relies on bushes and undergrowth for concealment, but in the desert this is simply not available, so camouflage techniques become even more important than usual.

Pay particular attention to changes in the terrain, both in shape and in colour, and make sure that camouflage is kept up to date.

Because the sun is so strong, shadows are very pronounced. Remember, they move as the sun moves. If you're using shadow to conceal a vehicle, for instance, make sure that you re-position it regularly. Use covering sheets rather than camouflage netting; the shade it will give is as valuable as the camouflage.

In sand deserts, where there are no breaks in the smooth nature of the terrain, it is actually impossible to

An M88 armoured recovery vehicle of the US Army speeds across the Egyptian desert. The harsh terrain conditions wear out equipment very quickly, so success in the desert is often dependent on good logistic support.

camouflage anything at all. It's also impossible to dig in. This works two ways, of course, and the enemy is just as vulnerable as you, but it does mean a complete change of operating methods. Occupation and any sort of static operation are impossible, and raiding is the only feasible means of coming to grips with the enemy forces.

Since computers became pocket-sized, in the mid-1970s, observation has changed from being something you do with your eyes to something you do much more effectively and at longer range with machines. Remote Sensing technology, including infra-red and low-light, is at its most useful in the desert at night.

Just because you see no signs of enemy presence, that doesn't mean you're not under observation from two or three kilometres away. Always observe strict concealment discipline, and remember that sound carries a long way in the desert, too.

Desert firefights can take place at over 1000 metres, well over the effective range of 5.56-mm rifles. Here a US paratrooper prepares to fire an FN Minimi light machine-gun from its bipod.

Above: Running into action on exercise. You cannot fight effectively in the desert if you are encumbered by a lot of personal equipment. You need water and ammunition.

Combat Report
Rhodesia: 'Fire Force' Mission

Frank Terrell, a former member of the Rhodesian Light Infantry, tells the story of a 'Fire Force' mission during the Rhodesian War.

In the early afternoon of 7 March 1979 I was one of 12 men from the RLI's Support Commando called out for the second time to an area near Gwanda, in southern Rhodesia. Following a short flight our three G-cars began to orbit a group of neat fields, flanked by craggy hills on one side and a small wooded area on the other. Before long it was decided to deploy callsign Stop-1 on their own, and to insert Stops 2 and 3 at the base of a rocky gomo (hill) on the edge of a mealie (corn) field.

While a K-car provided overhead cover, Corporal M. Robie's Stop-3 was put down, only to find itself involved in a firefight almost immediately; our G-car was forced to remain aloft while the K-car dealt with it, and we were then ordered to go in and reinforce Stop-3. As we banked to begin our descent we came under automatic fire from another terrorist, but the Alouette simply levelled out and thudded in to land opposite a treeline now occupied by Stop-3. We leapt out and doubled through the swirling cloud of red dust thrown up by the helicopter's rotors, to be met by two of Robie's men who were dragging along a terrorist killed by the K-car. The body was unceremoniously flung aboard the Alouette for transportation back to base, where it would later be photographed and fingerprinted by Special Branch.

The voice of command

As the chopper departed with its gruesome cargo, I positioned myself behind the negligible cover of a scrawny tree just as one of our troopers, Nick Webster, and Stop-2's gunner, Micky Maitland, both opened up. Everyone else joined in. The main target appeared to be a tree about 70 metres to our front-right, but Webster and Maitland were concentrating their fire against the mealie crop in the middle of the

field, well away from the tree! Unable to see anything worth shooting at, I refrained from firing. Webster and Maitland later confided that they had seen a terr running away from the tree, into the mealie field, but for some reason everyone else had decided to fire in the opposite direction to where the enemy had fled!

Then from out of the confusion came a voice of command: Corporal Robie yelled at us to stand up and follow him into the open towards the bullet-riddled tree. Heart pumping wildly, I followed the others in the dash across the carefully ploughed field. Immediately the earth to our front erupted in little puffs of dirt, but due to the sounds of our own weapons it was impossible to determine just by listening who was shooting at us.

We stared at the canister . . .

Somehow we reached our objective unscathed. Stop-3 threw themselves behind some rocks but I and the rest of Stop-2 were forced to lie in the open, between the rocks on our right and the dense rows of corn off to our left.

Although Corporal Robie had assumed command he was in fact outranked by Lieutenant Williams, a young subaltern who had joined the Commando just five days previously. To our horror, he now ordered Stop-2 further out into the clearing.

I relayed the officer's order to Nick on my left: 'Lieutenant Williams says you blokes are to spread out towards the mealie field!'

'You too, Terrell!' shouted Lieutenant Williams.

'Bollocks!' Webster screamed back.

'What did he say?' demanded Williams.

'They're not too keen on the idea, sir.'

'There's a bloody terr in that mealie field with an RPD, for Christ's sake! Tell him that!'

'Sir, there's a terr with a machine-gun in the mealie field!'

'Who says so?'

'Webster, sir. He saw him.'

'Rubbish! Spread out!'

'No!' yelled Webster.

'I don't think that's really a good idea, sir . . .'

'I'm telling you, stop bunching up and SPREAD OUT!'

We were often flown into action two or three times a day. Here a machine-gunner fires an FN MAG into the bush during a typical sweep.

Thankfully for us, the argument was never resolved, because Corporal Robie threw a WP grenade at the tree, believing it still concealed our terrorist. It thudded into the treetrunk and promptly bounced back to land smack in the middle of our little group. There was a sudden silence as we all stared at the green canister before burying our faces in the dry earth. A second later the grenade detonated in a dazzling display of blazing phosphorus. Remarkably, no-one was hurt!

Then we began a typical bush-clearance operation, climbing over the gomo, nervously firing into the dense undergrowth and tossing grenades into caves, never knowing where the enemy might choose to hide.

Suddenly Lance-Corporal Graham Gilbert shouted 'Check, check, check!'

I was just in time to 'check' two figures armed with AKs who had broken cover a hundred metres to our front. We all opened up simultaneously, six FN rifles and two MAGs sending a hail of deadly fire towards the unfortunate terrs, who quickly dived headlong into some long grass.

'Hold your fire!'

As we ran forward Corporal Robie directed a G-car towards the enemy position. We all watched as the Alouette hovered 10 feet above the bush, firing two Brownings into the thicket. He ceased firing and cautiously approached the spot and spread out in order to search for the floppies.

I dreaded this part of a sweep. Was he dead, or could he still be alive, perhaps even peering down the sights of his weapon at this very moment? Levelling my rifle, I peered through the leafy branches. Suddenly from the other side of the bush there came a yell, instantly followed by several rounds which burst through the thicket, narrowly missing me.

I ducked down, screaming 'Hold your fire! Hold your fire!'

The shooting abruptly stopped and an anxious Lance-Corporal Gilbert appeared.

'What,' he spluttered, 'are you doing there?'

'What do you bloody think?'

It was quite ridiculous. The tension was relieved a moment later when someone pulled a body from beneath the bush. It was the other terr, his face smashed from the G-car's burst of fire.

We dumped the bodies together in a clearing and waited for the G-cars. Idly, I pulled up a trouser leg to scratch an itch. Glancing down, I saw that my leg above my jump-boot was covered with tiny black parasites: cattle ticks! Looking around, I noticed that the ground we were sitting on was crawling with them . . . and now so were we!

Members of the 1 RLI waiting to be flown into action in 1979. Towards the end of the Rhodesian war we virtually monopolized the Fire Force system of operations.

ON THE ATTACK

Charlie Troop's four APCs were hull-down in a stony depression. Schultz stuck his head up very cautiously and took a long look right round the horizon, and then concentrated on the patch of ground a little off to his right, where the Remote Sensing helo had said he'd seen hot spots. It was difficult to tell in the heat of the morning: lots of ground-level haze and mirage. But slowly Schultz began to make out short, unnaturally straight lines, vertical and horizontal, that could only be vehicles, and knew he had them.

The desert is, in general, a featureless place. In military terms that means there's very little key terrain, so

The M60 is the highest Main Battle Tank in the world. One of the few occasions when this is useful is in the desert, where a US tank commander can see further than the crew of a smaller, Soviet tank. However, the Israelis who have used M60s in desert warfare have abandoned the high cupola seen here.

static defensive operations tied to a particular feature are rare. Both attack and defence are likely to be exercises in mobility, and the force that moves most effectively, and protects its supply lines, is likely to come out the winner.

Enemy weaknesses

When you probe enemy positions prior to setting up an attack strategy, you're looking for weaknesses. Sometimes they're local – small pockets not as well prepared or as well supported as others – and sometimes they're large. In the desert it often happens that the enemy defensive force is weaker on one flank than on the other, because its commanders have decided to concentrate on a threat

coming from one particular direction and don't have enough strength to keep up all-round defence.

If patrol activity and air reconnaissance establish this to be the case, then the answer is rapid deployment. Hit that sector hard and fast, and try to achieve a penetration in depth before the enemy can block the move with mobile reserves.

Once you're through the front line of his defences, go for the supply and communications lines. With those cut, he can't last long as an effective

Inside an M60 in Egypt: the desert sun has heated the tank hull so much that you can literally fry an egg on it. The Israelis have developed lightweight flame retardant tank crew uniforms but this American tank commander wears the basic lightweight desert uniform.

Left: The open terrain of the desert makes air defence vital for any ground forces. Here an Iraqi anti-aircraft gunner shows off his Soviet DSh K-38 12.7-mm machine-gun: note the size of the rounds.

fighting force, and there's not much cover for him to sneak away under. Make sure your PoW holding area is big enough; in desert operations, prisoners often come in large numbers.

Successful offensive operations in the desert depend on speed and aggression, and adequate defensive positions are hard to come by, so you can bet that in many cases the enemy is going to rely on attack as being the best means of defence. The result will be a fast and fluid operation involving two attacking forces, both searching for the other's weak flank. The winner is likely to be the one who finds it first.

Up-to-date intelligence and secure communications channels are really important in this sort of running fight. If the attack unit commander doesn't know exactly what's going on at any given moment, he won't be able to exploit the successes his troops are having.

Even in this type of skirmishing operation, you have to follow the basic rules. The operation divides up into three parts:

1 Movement to contact
2 Hasty or deliberate attack
3 Exploitation or pursuit

The formula applies whether you're the lead company for a divisional attack, or a squad operating out on your own.

There's no substitute for aggressive reconnaissance. Depending on your position, this may have to be to your 'rear' as well as to the front and on the flanks. A moving force is at a disadvantage in the desert because the country is so open and observation so easy.

Long-range reconnaissance

It's usually a good idea to push reconnaissance patrols out a long way, so that they don't give away the position of the main force. They also act as early warning, and deny the enemy the chance to get a close look at what's going on.

Accurate reporting is really essential. In the desert it's as well not to rely on exception reports – sending back information only when something of note happens. Because of the long distances involved, a negative report

THE DESERT WAR

Deserts comprise one-fifth of the world's land surface, and most of them are strategically important. Desert operations require specialist equipment, specialist training and acclimatisation, and above all a high degree of self-discipline. The desert is harsh and living conditions very uncomfortable, but the aim does not change: you must not only survive, but close with and kill the enemy.

Reflections and observation
Forces in the desert are often revealed to the enemy by windscreens or optics reflecting the light. The ideal observation position is on high ground with the sun behind you. If possible, attack at dawn from out of the sun.

Tank gunnery range
The flat desert terrain sometimes allows tank use their main armame very long ranges. Altho the average range of ta actions in the 1973 Ara Israeli war was under 1 metres, in the 1982 inv of Lebanon Israeli Mer successfully engaged S tanks at over 2000 me

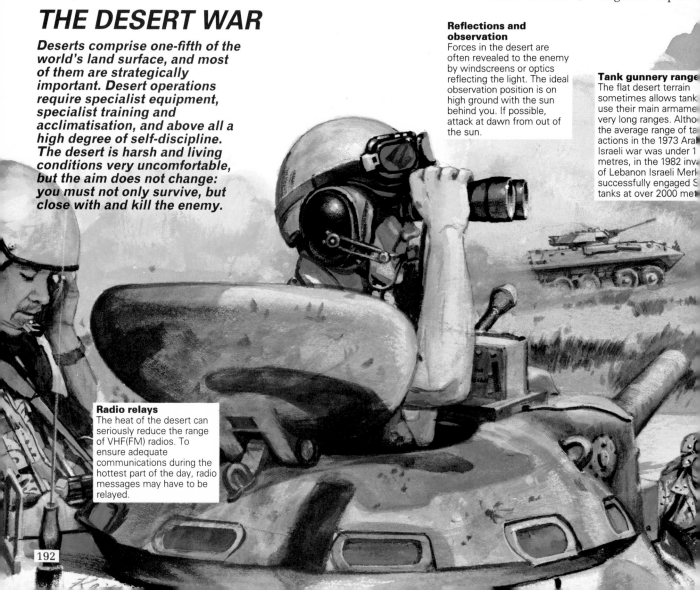

Radio relays
The heat of the desert can seriously reduce the range of VHF(FM) radios. To ensure adequate communications during the hottest part of the day, radio messages may have to be relayed.

Aeroscouts
This one has found the enemy the hard way: flying NOE (nap-of-earth) you are not necessarily going to spot the enemy more easily than a ground observer. Stationary targets are the most difficult to see as there is little to draw your attention – but if you are not alert it is easy to blunder into enemy anti-aircraft defences.

Dismount and scan
Instead of observing from a moving helicopter, which itself kicks up a cloud of dust when flying low, land between 5 and 10km from your target area and observe from the ground. Repeat the process until you make contact. This reduces the danger of accidentally flying into range of SAMs and AAA batteries.

Dust deception
Use dust to your advantage: helicopters flying NOE or jeeps towing chains kick up enough dust to look like a major troop concentration. Keep the enemy guessing where your real attack is coming from.

bility
cal mobility is the key ccessful desert ations. With few acles to movement, nd troops can oeuvre with the dom of a naval task e. Speed of execution is ntial and requires self-ained mechanised or obile forces with ellent communications.

Attack upwind
In windy conditions often encountered in the desert, moving vehicles kick up substantial dust clouds, which can mask the fire of other friendly forces unless you remember to have the moving elements upwind of those providing covering fire.

Staggered movement
Any form of desert movement creates dust. Moving directly across country on the hardest ground reduces dust clouds, but vehicles should not follow each other unless you think you are threatened by mines.

Gun barrel bend
Because the top of the tank's gun barrel is exposed to the full force of the desert sun while the bottom of the barrel is in the shade, the barrel will droop slightly. This reduces long-range accuracy. It can correct itself after the firing of a few rounds, which will produce uniform temperature in the barrel, but you may need to re-boresight the gun.

Scouting forces
US Marine Corps Light Armoured Vehicles race into action covered by the 105-mm guns of M60 tanks. Scouting elements should be 2000-4000 metres away from the main body and must be deployed all around your force, not just at the front. In desert warfare, you must be ready for contact from any side.

may be as useful as a sighting. Be careful not to clog up the communications channels with trivia, though.

Don't forget the possibility of deceiving the enemy by means of reconnaissance patrols sent out for just that purpose. Patrols are inevitably going to be discovered and observed. By trying to figure out what they're up to and where they came from, the enemy commanders are going to try to put together a picture of what you're doing in the area. Sending out patrols to reconnoitre an area in which you have no real tactical interest could be enough to get him to commit defensive forces to an area miles away from the one you actually intend to attack.

Enemy strengths and weaknesses

The reconnaissance patrol's job is to bring back accurate reports of the enemy's position, deployment and strength. Where is he? How many men

These Soviet-supplied M46 130-mm guns of the Iraqi army are seen in Soviet-style linear deployment. The guns are about 40 metres apart, the whole six-gun battery taking up about 250 metres. It is positioned behind a line of low hills and is invisible to the Iranian attackers.

has he got? How are they distributed? How are they armed? Do they have adequate reserves and supply channels? Can you get round them and cut their supply, wait for them to exhaust themselves and mop them up?

An attack in strength will probably require troop concentration. If the enemy has any powers of observation at all, he's going to notice this, and realise what's going on. Make all your movements at night, and still observe concealment disciplines to try to outwit passive light gathering devices and infra-red snoopers.

The enemy is going to try to stop your attack with firepower, obstacles and counter-attacks. Your best chance to stop him doing that lies in taking

out his surveillance equipment and his heavy weapons, and the best way to do it is with attack helicopters and fixed-wing airstrike.

Win air superiority and keep it. Then you'll be able to take out his armour and anti-armour, and as every desert campaign since World War I has shown, that's the key to victory.

The desert is excellent tank country. Get them before they can get moving, preferably by means of air strikes. Just in case the enemy armour does break out, make sure your anti-tank crews are right up to strength and have plenty of practice at long-range operations.

The weather conditions will possibly degrade the performance of ATGMs, and their ability to aim accurately will certainly be impaired by heat haze and mirage if they're close to the ground. ATGM crews should be sited up high whenever possible.

Shock, overwhelm and destroy

The desert is no place to hang about in a protracted attack that gets bogged down. Re-supply is too difficult, and the weather conditions too mean, to allow a long-drawn-out attack to succeed. The faster you can put together an attack in sufficient strength to make a hole in an enemy defensive position, get through to his supply lines and cut them, the quicker the whole thing will be over. This means:

1 Accurate reconnaissance
2 Accurate navigation
3 Speed
4 Violence
5 Reinforcement
6 Equipment and weapons

Once the reconnaissance patrols have found an exploitable gap in the enemy position, use it. Widen it so that units of the attack force can leapfrog and give each other covering fire. The enemy is likely to use improvised obstacles wherever he can, so make sure that equipment is available to deal with them fast and effectively.

Use the environment

Whenever possible, attack should come from out of the sun. Not only will the attack force see the defenders clearly, without any shadow to get in the way, but they, in their turn, will benefit from the effects of glare and mirage.

Don't get bogged down in this principle, though. Surprise is still the most important factor, and it may be that the defending enemy will be keeping a

SOVIET-TYPE DESERT WAR PLATOON STRONGPOINT

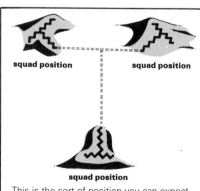

squad position   **squad position**

squad position

This is the sort of position you can expect to find Soviet-trained and supplied armies using in the desert. It will include anti-tank weapons and will probably be protected by mines. The individual squad trenches will be deep enough to withstand a heavy concentration of artillery fire.

SOVIET-TYPE TANK/ APC STRONGPOINT

You may face a more elaborate defensive position near key terrain features such as passes through mountainous areas. This sort of position is as 'tank proof' as they can make it, and if you cannot bypass it there is no option but to make a full-scale infantry attack.

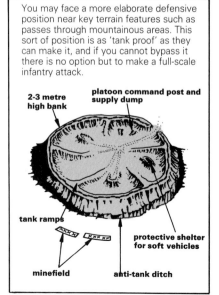

2-3 metre high bank

platoon command post and supply dump

tank ramps

protective shelter for soft vehicles

minefield   **anti-tank ditch**

specially close watch on the sector facing into the sun.

To a highly mobile force, dust can be a major problem unless there's enough wind to disperse it. Move in echelon – behind and to the side of the unit in front – with the overwatching element upwind of the moving element.

Dust obstacle

Remember that dust can mask movement almost as effectively as smoke, though you can't control it as well. It can be a particular obstacle to laser aiming devices, and helicopters in particular have to take care not to mask their target acquisition and designation system with dust kicked up by rotor downwash.

Night-time visibility in the desert varies a lot with the time of the month. When the moon is close to full, visibility is surprisingly good, even small details standing out clearly. At the

THERMAL IMAGE OF A TANK AT NIGHT

A thermal sensor builds up a picture of a target by detecting heat emissions. It relies on the temperature differences between a target and its surroundings; the greater the contrast, the better the image. It is of little value during daylight hours in the desert, but is very useful at night because the enemy cannot detect it. The desert night is very cold and operational vehicles likely to be warm, so remember to shield any heat emission sources during the night.

Note: track and roadwheels show up clearly. The tank has not fired its armament recently so the gun barrel does not show up.

Above: Combined arms attack by Israeli armour and F-4 Phantom jets during the 1973 Arab-Israeli war. Close integration of air and armour during the Sinai campaign enabled the Israelis to cross the Suez Canal and win the war.

Above: A member of a Combat Control team prepares a landing zone for the 82nd Airborne Division. The 'beach buggy' is a very practical answer to high mobility over the stony desert.

other side of the lunar period, the nights are as dark as you can imagine. At times of no moon, even passive night vision aids, that work by collecting and enhancing the small amount of light available, are next to useless. Only thermal imaging (infra-red) devices work satisfactorily.

Sandstorm danger

Sandstorms cut visibility to just a couple of metres, too, and may make it necessary for operations to be halted. If an advancing unit is caught in a sandstorm blowing from the enemy position, the safest course is to sit tight until it's over. Remember that in those circumstances the enemy will get visibility back before you will, and that you may get caught by surprise as a result.

Below: During the 1973 Arab-Israeli war the Israelis made extensive use of these M3 half-tracks carrying TCM-20 twin 20-mm anti-aircraft guns. They serve to defend convoys and choke points like the canal crossings from enemy air attack.

Combat Report
Vietnam:
Long Range Reconnaissance Platoon

Mike Glendon served in the Australian Army and did two tours in Vietnam. Here he describes a joint operation in 1969 with the US 11th Armored Cavalry Regiment.

Our Long Range Reconnaissance Platoon had been working with the US 11th Armored Cavalry for about 10 days: nothing but false alarms and boredom, with the usual army attitude of 'hurry up and wait'. The false alarms were the most tiring of all, because you could never tell what was happening.

In first-degree jungle you cannot move with any speed at all; you advance at about 300-500 metres per hour. If your platoon commander is in his usual position in the middle of the column, he has to rely on information sent back by his lead scouts. But when you have 15 or 20 men firing automatic weapons plus enemy soldiers returning fire, you cannot communicate verbally; besides, you're too busy and too damn' scared.

By the time the Viet Cong hit us we had had two or three false alarms and were not in a friendly mood. The quickest way to clear a group of soldiers off the top of an APC (Armoured Personnel Carrier) is to open up with a heavy machine-gun, and at about 3 o'clock in the afternoon this is what the Viet Cong did to the APC in front of me. In a matter of seconds we were on the ground returning fire.

Sweeping through the VC

The Americans all joined in with their usual enthusiasm for automatic firearms. I will always remember looking up at one of the APCs and seeing a machine-gunner standing on the top of the vehicle, firing from the hip. I knew him as a quiet sort of guy; something or someone had definitely pissed him off.

I knew I had to get a flanking section out to the left to sweep through the VC position, but trying to get this message across while under fire was difficult, to say the least. I was about to give up and let the Cavalry do the sweep when the VC fire got very accurate and two of my men went down.

I realized that if I wasn't to lose any more men I had to get our two nearest APCs to fire on the VC positions to our front with their heavy .50 and .30 calibre machine-guns, but they were concentrating their fire on our right. What I did next is something I will never understand to this day: I took one of my hand grenades, left the pin in, and lobbed it at the nearest APC.

It landed right in front of one of the machine-gunners. As you can imagine, I caught his attention, and I can only guess at the state of his underclothes afterwards.

Using sign language that definitely isn't in the military handbook, I managed to make him

understand what I wanted, and within seconds we were being covered by the .50 cals from two APCs. This gave me the chance I wanted. I moved one section round to my left flank and soon they were on the move, hopefully cutting off one of the VCs' exits.

A shout from the sweep told me to move up to them. When we arrived, the usual scene greeted us – a weapon or two, plenty of bloodstains, but no enemy KIA (Killed in Action). It was standard practice to remove their dead so that didn't surprise us.

While all this was going on our medical Dustoff chopper was waiting to evacuate our two wounded. We gave him the word that the LZ was cold, and before I knew it he was down and the wounded were away. The courage, speed and sympathy of the Dustoff crews never ceased to amaze me, and no words can express my gratitude to all of them.

After any firefight it is advisable to let the men settle down for a smoke before saddling up again; we always did, to get our thoughts together. This went for the US troops too but, hell, didn't they go funny after their smokes!

Half an hour later we were on the way back to our FSB (Fire Support Base), looking forward to a hot meal and a bit of security. We were to be disappointed.

There are many times during Army training when you wonder why in God's name you are being taught things that seem a total waste of time: 'standing to' and 'standing down' are prime examples.

'Standing to' is when an army unit in a field position prepares for an attack, with all personnel standing in their pits with all their webbing gear on and rifles at the ready. This is done at dusk and at dawn, because it is generally thought that the enemy will attack when you are at your most vulnerable. Most soldiers hated stand-to, especially in the morning, but this time we were all grateful for our training.

The attack

The attack came when our platoon commander was just finishing briefing us on what was to happen the next day. It started with a very loud crack. At first we thought it was one of the US artillery pieces opening up, which they did frequently on their H & I (Harassment and Interdiction) missions. Then came one of the most dreadful sounds an infantryman can hear: the yell of ''INCOMING!''

The crack was the sound of a VC recoilless rifle and the round going over us at a massive velocity. Then they put down a hell of a barrage, but luckily they didn't get our range immediately. In seconds we were all in our personal pits but not returning fire, as we couldn't see anything to shoot at.

This didn't deter the US 11th Armored Cavalry from opening up with everything they had, and for a while it seemed like there

was a competition going on between the VC and the Americans over who had more weapons. The initial mortar attack went on for five or six minutes and the only casualty I saw was an American trooper, who got zapped off an APC after a mortar round blew up in front of him.

It was when I was crawling from one pit to another that the VC really decided to get serious. When I next looked up, the whole sky was lit by green communist tracer rounds and you could just make out the VC silhouettes as they approached.

Returning fire with an automatic weapon is a great remedy for this sort of situation, and that's precisely what I was doing from behind an APC. I must have used up at least two magazines when I saw, about 25 yards away, a VC sweep the top of another APC with his AK-47, killing the whole crew.

They thought I was dead

I decided to move quickly, as an APC in this position is highly vulnerable. I don't remember the run I made to the nearest gun pit in our platoon; all I remember is finding myself upside down with red-hot empty casings falling on my face and being called all sorts of bastards by the other two occupants, whose skulls I had nearly smashed when I dived in.

I eventually untangled myself, looked around to see what the hell was going on and, to my horror, saw an NVA (North Vietnamese soldier) with his AK pointing at what seemed liked right between my eyes. But before I could take it all in, he'd gone.

I turned to tell whoever was in the pit with me that we weren't up against VC but NVA and saw, to my horror, that the enemy soldier had succeeded in claiming his victim. After that I went into the firefight with a rage I was to experience many times after seeing my friends killed and horribly wounded in Vietnam.

The rest of that terrible evening was a variety of incidents and nightmares: I pointed my M16, a body dropped, I pointed it again, there was a scream . . . no need to go into gory details. Then, suddenly, it stopped: no warning, nothing just silence.

It was at this point that I think I broke the world's high jump record. The silence had lasted for about 15-20 seconds, and all I wanted was to get away from the dead body beside me. I was climbing out of the pit when ''Puff the Magic Dragon'' – an American AC-47 gunship – opened up. To this day I sincerely believe I jumped vertically, with no run-up, about 25 feet in the air and landed back in the pit, keeping a corpse company.

I eventually settled down and the tears started; with them came the shakes. That dugout became my hell and that's where I was found covered in dirt and blood. My rescuers thought I was dead; at the time, I wished I was.

M113 APCs of the US 11th Armored Cavalry carried a pair of M60 7.62-mm machine guns on the sides and a Browning .50-cal up front. To the VC they were 'Green Dragons.'

We used many weapons in Vietnam. The nearer soldier is firing the Australian version of the FN FAL. The other bloke has an American M16.

DEFENDING YOUR POSITION

THE IMPORTANCE OF RECONNAISSANCE

Recce forces must establish:

1. What is the enemy's short term objective?
2. What are the enemy's avenues of approach and what forces are employed on them?
3. Are the apparent movements feints or the real thing?

Once these questions are answered you can manoeuvre and destroy the enemy, but until they are confirmed you can do little. This is doubly dangerous in desert warfare because the side with the greatest potential for manoeuvre is more likely to win.

A US gun crew loads the charge into an M198 155-mm howitzer. A mobile defence is better than a static one in the desert, since the enemy can usually outflank you. The long-range firepower of 155-mm guns can cover a withdrawal and even lay mines in the path of the enemy using special-purpose ammunition.

Schultz brought Charlie Troop's APCs back into the dry wadi at speed, keeping to the stones to avoid throwing up too much dust. He looked around at the camouflaged APCs of Alpha and Bravo Troops and signalled his drivers to complete the company's defensive perimeter, and ran over to where the other two troop leaders were squatting, a map weighed down with rocks on the ground between them.

He said nothing, but drew two lines on the map with a finger: the two enemy armoured columns he'd seen in the course of the reconnaissance patrol. The two lines met close to their position.

"Oh,****," said Bayliss, with a lot of feeling.

Defence is normally characterised by waiting for the enemy to come to you rather than going out to look for him, and that's true in the desert too, even though the fight itself may be between two moving forces instead of the defending force staying put in one place and trying to stop the enemy from taking it. With this in mind, camouflage and concealment of your vehicles and installations is very important.

The first thing to look at is the colour of the vehicles and equipment. Does it match the surroundings? If it doesn't, then re-paint it. Every unit of company strength in the US Army is issued with a paint spray gun and a range of matt paints of suitable colours.

Check your camouflage

The most useful camouflage "tool" is the net or cloth. The standard net, used in temperate climates, is wide mesh, decorated with narrow coloured strips of cloth running in different directions. These strips of cloth cast irregular shadows that break up the outline of the objects underneath. And they don't work in the desert.

The US Army has developed what it calls the Light Weight Camouflage Screening System (LWCSS) in its place. This is a close-weave mesh that gives cover from visual observation and infra-red and radar surveillance. It's essential that the object to be hidden is covered completely, because the LWCSS depends on imitating the colour and texture of the terrain.

If all you've got is wide mesh camo netting, then the best results will be obtained by stitching open-weave cloth to it and using it mesh side up, to give a rough texture. Radar-reflecting plastic, spray painted to match the local colour, can be added as "gar-nish", as can strips of sacking.

Make sure that nets and camo cloths are big enough to cover the area completely without having to pull it tight over the poles. Peg it out loosely all around, allowing a gradual slope of not more than 15 degrees.

Vehicle tracks

Unless and until the wind blows, you're going to have a problem with vehicle tracks. Obliterate them, or you're just leaving a signpost for any passing enemy close-support aircraft to hit you with an airstrike.

Camouflage is the first thing you see to when a vehicle stops for any length of time. Follow this procedure:

1 Stop the vehicle in shadow or vegetation, if possible.
2 Mask windscreens and other shiny surfaces and areas of deep shadow with sacking screens.
3 Drape the camo netting and peg it out.
4 Add vegetation and other garnish to the net.
5 Blot out vehicle tracks.

US Army M60 tanks live firing during desert warfare exercises in Egypt. Because of the amount of dust raised by armoured vehicles moving and firing, it is often difficult for gunners to observe their shell strike.

Tank gunnery techniques

Standard range adjustment

When you cannot clearly see the fall of shot, apply standard range adjustment until you bracket the target. The standard adjustment is + or − 200 metres at up to 1500 metres, and + or − 400 metres at longer ranges. If a tank platoon operates together like this it can get rounds on target faster than if the vehicles fought independently.

← **wind direction**

All three tanks begin with the same ammunition loaded and the same range set.

This tank observes the fire of the first tank and applies the standard method of adjustment, then fires at the same target. After firing it pulls back behind the crest.

This tank fires and misses, then withdraws behind the crest of the hill.

The third tank in the platoon observes from the turret-down position, only the cupola and commander's head projecting above the crest.

Burst on target method

This method is faster because the gunner operates without further reference to the tank commander. He notes where the shell lands using the target reticle on his sight, adjusts his aim, and fires again.

← **wind direction**

This tank fires first.

60 metres

The gunner in this tank spots where the shell lands using his target reticle, adjusts his aim and fires.

Aircraft, and especially helicopters, are more difficult to conceal than vehicles, not just because they're bigger but also because they're more fragile. But they have such a great strategic value that the job must be done both quickly and effectively.

Quick close-down

The pilot will approach the landing site, hidden by the terrain from enemy observation wherever possible. Once on the ground, the aircraft should be closed down straight away, to keep the delicate moving parts safe from dust damage.

Then cover all reflecting surfaces with sacking, and push or tow it into shadow if you can. Turn the main rotor by hand until it's at 45 degrees to the fuselage, then peg it down to the ground, forming a sort of umbrella frame over which the camo netting can be spread.

Vehicles and aircraft should never be bunched up together, nor should they be allowed too close to command

The open terrain of the desert allows GPMGs to be used in the Sustained Fire role up to about 1800 metres. Well-placed machine-gun nests can prevent enemy infantry from making a successful dismounted assault and keep them out of effective rifle range. This is an Iraqi machine-gun post using a Soviet PKM GPMG.

route from one sangar to another for a day or two can cause a track that's visible from the air under the right circumstances.

The larger the object, the more difficult it is to hide. So what do you do with something the size of a supply dump? The quick answer is to disperse it as widely as possible; the long-term answer is probably to bury it. One thing that's important to remember when storing supplies, whether it's for a small unit or an entire army, is to mix the contents of each section of the dump. That way you won't lose all of one commodity if one dump gets hit.

Defensive positions

Normally, you fight a defensive action to retain a particular piece of ground. In the desert, that's seldom the case; instead, destruction of enemy forces is the primary aim. There is, as the US Army's Desert Fighting Manual puts it, "no more sense in occupying large areas of desert than there would be in occupying a patch of sea."

posts or other permanent sites. Three or four hundred metres is quite close enough.

One of the things to look for in selecting a defensive position or dispersal area is the type of soil: it must allow you to dig in. All holes, no matter how permanent, must be covered to prevent the shadow they cast giving away their position. Any vehicle that's going to stay in one place for more than 24 hours should be dug in, too.

Keep discipline

It's all too easy to forget about discipline if you've been in one place for a day or two. There is no short cut to security. Bad camo discipline can kill you and everybody around you. Even something as stupid as using the same

South West African Territorial Force troops deploy a mortar for action: in this sort of terrain, concealed defensive positions are very hard to achieve. Only fast-moving, mobile forces will achieve success in the desert.

Combat Skills

Mobility and manoeuvrability are the keys to desert defence. You will rarely build a strongpoint or fire base to defend a particular feature such as an oasis, and even if you do you'll try to get most of your work done well out in front, to inflict enough damage on the enemy so that he won't ever get to the critical area at all.

Open country is tank country, and the desert is more open than any other. Because there is little or no local cover, your anti-armour crews have to operate at long range if they're going to escape the enemy tank force's infantry curtain. This means that your defence will be centred around your heavier infantry anti-tank weapons, anti-tank guided missiles, shorter-range LAWs and other lightweight kit. This might succeed in damaging the target, but will give away the fire team's position, so if you have to use them, use as much fire support as possible and don't hang around in one place too long.

Strongpoints

There may come a time when you do want to deny a particular position to the enemy, and in this case camouflage and concealment go by the board. The emphasis will instead be on security, both from air attack and from surface forces.

By definition, a strongpoint is going to be isolated, cut off from outside assistance and re-supply except by air. Unless you have complete air superiority it's vulnerable to air strikes and artillery bombardment as well as direct assault.

Wherever possible the enemy will try to by-pass strongpoints, hoping to

An SA-2 SAM site overrun by Israeli forces during the 1973 Yom Kippur war. The problem with static defensive positions is that, in the desert, they are often easily bypassed and you can find yourself surrounded.

An M163 20-mm Vulcan cannon deployed for anti-aircraft defence: due to the air threat in the desert, always disperse your vehicles in irregular patterns and dig them in when possible.

starve you out and mop you up later, and that's probably the chief danger, but the feature you're defending may be important enough for him to take the trouble to assault the position.

He'll try to get up close by stealth, attacking at night or under cover of a sandstorm, so the first priority is warning devices. Minefields strung with tangle-foot and concertina wire, fitted with flares and audible warning devices triggered by any attempt to tamper with it, will tell you of any approach. Inside that comes an anti-

tank ditch. Make sure it's deep enough and wide enough to do the job. Inside the ditch, and right up tight against it, comes the main defensive wall.

As long as the strongpoint is not overlooked by commanding high ground, enemy armour will stand very little chance of coming close enough

What happens when you neglect your air defence: an Egyptian column destroyed in the Mitla Pass by Israeli air strikes during the Six Day War. Note the mixture of Soviet armour – a T-34 with an SU-100 behind and T-54s in the background.

to support its infantry. Your ATGMs and light anti-tank weapons, sited in protected positions in or on the main defensive wall, will be in a commanding position, and the enemy's infantry won't be able to get anywhere near.

The enemy is more likely to leave his armour out at maximum range and use it as mobile artillery. He'll rely on that and mortar fire to try to win fire superiority, so that his assault infantry can try to get in close to breach the integrity of the defensive wall.

The only chance he's got is to come in under cover of bad visibility, either natural or man-made. You should lay down interlocking arcs of fire, with machine-guns working within fixed limits, to ensure that assault troops will be stopped even if you can't actually see them.

The chief danger in defending a strongpoint lies in running short of supplies. As long as you have enough food, water and ammunition to see you through to the next re-supply and are sufficiently well protected from air strike and artillery bombardment, taking you out will be a very expensive business indeed.

Egyptian marines deploy a DSh K-38 12.7-mm machine-gun on an old Sokolov mount. Rifles and machine-guns should be oiled sparingly or they will clog up with sand: you have been warned.

4 Firing *first* and *accurately* is the key to success in desert war, particularly now that tank versus tank engagements are likely to be decided in two shots.
5 Make maximum use of markers such as rocks or poles to designate sectors of fire on the ground and to mark your own withdrawal routes and routes between battle positions.
6 Anti-tank guided missiles like TOW will be prevented from using their maximum range if they are sited at ground level, where heat haze is worst. They need to be several metres above the desert floor if possible, so minor undulations can be very important.
7 When calling down indirect artillery fire it is better to overestimate the range rather than underestimate. If the first ranging shell lands short it may throw up enough sand and smoke to obscure the target and prevent you bringing down accurate fire.

Unarmed Combat Course No. 11

CONTROLLING THE ATTACKER ON THE GROUND

It is important that you are familiar with the basic techniques of ground holds. Once controlled on the ground your options are very limited, so if the fight does end up there it must be you who does the controlling. There are many techniques for controlling someone on the ground; the following are simple and effective.

Roll the attacker off

1 The attacker has pinned you to the ground and is sitting astride you, choking you with both hands.

2 Force your left hand over his arm and grab his collar.

3 Bring your right hand over his arm to join your left hand and begin to choke the attacker.

4 Roll to your left, pulling the attacker over onto his back, breaking his hold. Remember to release your opponent in a practice session as soon as he is off you.

The defensive position

1 If you have no other option, this defensive position gives the most protection until an opportunity occurs.

2 Keep your hands ready to grab the attacker. Here he has reached over to grab you around the waist: this is your chance.

3 Grab the attacker's sleeve and pull sharply to make him lose balance. He will roll over your back.

4 Continue the motion so that you can put him in a rear hold, with your left hand on the attacker's left thigh and your right arm controlling his right arm.

The upper hold

1 Lying at the attacker's upper end, pass your right arm under his armpit and grab his collar. Your left arm does the same on the other side.

2 With both hands holding the attacker's collar, keep your hips low to the ground and your feet spread wide. The pressure will control the attacker's head.

Unarmed Combat Course No. 12
DEFENCE AGAINST KNIFE ATTACK
PART 1: USING IMPROVISED WEAPONS

If you are attacked with a knife, try to keep a good distance from the attacker. Defences against knife attack require plenty of room, so don't get backed into a corner. Look to see whether the knife is held ready for slashing or stabbing and plan your move. Remember: *Never practise these moves with a real knife.*

Facing the knife man

The slash
The knife held for slashing from side to side.

The plunge
The knife held for a downward stabbing movement, e.g. against your upper body.

The thrust
The knife ready for an upward thrust, e.g. against your stomach.

The attacker with the knife thinks he has the advantage, so you should encourage this; a 'wimpish' response will make him over-confident and lull him into a false sense of security.

Blocking with a rolled-up magazine

1 You need have no scruples about using an improvised weapon to defend yourself against knife attack.

2 A thick, glossy magazine tightly rolled up is strong enough to successfully block a stabbing attack.

3 Strike the attacker's wrist with the magazine to block the blow. You can then follow up using either the magazine or a blow with your other arm or legs.

Using a chair as an improvised defence

1 Use anything that comes to hand. A chair is an excellent defensive weapon: have confidence and think of its legs as four stabbing weapons.

2 Use it to block the attacker's moves, in this case a knife thrust, and try to force him towards a wall or other obstacle.

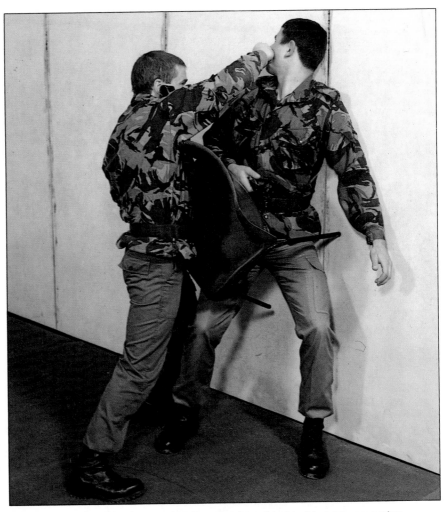

3 Strike hard against the attacker, forcing him against the wall, and don't forget to use your free hand to punch him in the face. The chair legs can be used to stab him in any vulnerable area.

4 The magazine makes a very effective weapon both for the initial block and for a counter-attack. Alternatives include big torches or rolled-up umbrellas.

Loose coins defence

A handful of change, stones or sand can be used to distract the attacker long enough for you to make your getaway. Fling them in his face as hard as you can.

Unarmed Combat Course No. 13

DEFENCE AGAINST KNIFE ATTACK WITHOUT WEAPONS

The following techniques are for use against a knife-armed attacker when you have no weapon of any kind with which to defend yourself. REMEMBER: YOU MUST NEVER USE A REAL KNIFE WHEN PRACTISING.

DEFENCE AGAINST A SLASH ATTACK (1)

1 The attacker prepares to slash you with his knife. Watch his shoulder carefully: it will begin to move before the knife does.

2 Block the knife attack using your left forearm against his wrist and forearm.

3 Follow up with the heel of your hand against his chin and, if possible, knee him in the testicles.

4 Deliver each blow with full force. This should give you time to disarm the attacker.

DEFENCE AGAINST A SLASH ATTACK (2)

1 The attacker prepares to slash you with his knife, this time attacking from left to right.

206

DEFENCE AGAINST A STAB FROM BELOW

1 The attacker stabs at you from below. You immediately shoot your vital parts to the rear and cross your wrists.

2 With the right arm on top, thrust your arms downwards to block the attacker's wrist.

3 Place your thumbs on the back of his hand and your fingers on the inside to apply a wristlock. If necessary follow up with a kick, then seize the weapon.

2 Block the attacker's arm using your left forearm. Bring your right arm up in the same way.

3 Seize the attacker's wrist and apply an outside wristlock. Remember to keep both your thumbs on the back of his hand.

4 Vigorously twisting him over should bring the attacker to the floor and force him to drop the knife.

Firing the SA8

The British Army

new combat rif

The British Army's ultra-modern new rifle, SA80, is arguably the best service rifle n available. The SA80's revolutionary featu give the individual infantryman an unp cedented degree of deadly accurate firepo in a weapon that's incredibly tough, simple maintain, and a pleasure to handle. The n striking feature of the SA80 is its 'b pup' configuration. The whole len of the gun consists of working pa with a padded shoulder rest at the r end.

The magazine sits behind the t ger so that a long barrel can be fit into a short overall length. The SA8 barrel is only a little shorter than SLR L1A1 rifle it replaces, but is per cent shorter. As a result, weapon is extremely easy to hanc especially in confined spaces, wh the magazine, sitting close in to body, can be changed with a lot l effort than on a conventional weape

The introduction of the SA80 will dramatically improve the firepower of British infantry. Far more accurate than the old Self-Loading Rifle and with the capacity for fully automatic fire, the SA80 is a match for any service rifle in the world.

House to house fighter

All these are important advanta for the British soldier: chargi through a doorway in Belfast with long SLR was never easy, whereas SA80's stubbiness makes it ideal house-to-house fighting. And carryi the weapon is no problem at all.

The SA80's sling arrangement I delighted the men who have to li with the weapon. The rifle can hung across the chest, back, or do one side, leaving the hands free. He ing the SLR with one hand in a 'n threatening posture' while on stre patrol in Northern Ireland was dious and tiring – and is now a thi of the past. The SA80's sling al means that the weapon doesn't get the way when hacking through jung snow, or forest, but it still com swiftly into action, simply by uncli ping the sling at the top. The sli then stays put on the shoulder, out the way.

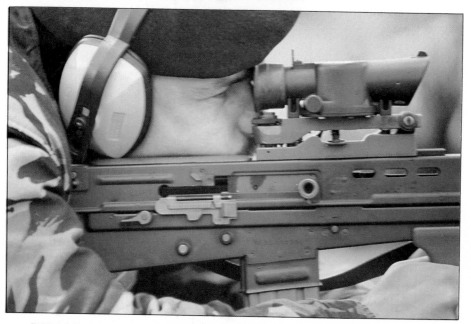

British infantry are receiving the SA80 with an optical sight, the SUSAT, which provides ×4 magnification. This is a tremendous aid to accuracy, especially when shooting in poor light conditions.

British troops will be issued with a magazine produced by **Royal Ordnance**, but the **SA80** is capable of using the same magazine as the **American M16**.

Above: The SA80 enables an average soldier to shoot to a very high standard, thanks to its sight, low recoil and simplicity of operation.

The **SA80** fires the new **NATO 5.56-mm** round, and it is planned that each soldier will have eight 30-round magazines plus a bandolier of ammo to re-charge them in the field.

With the **SA80**, your shoulder receives nothing like the kick delivered by the **SLR**. This improves accuracy, since soldiers firing the **SLR** tended to tense up while awaiting the recoil, which made for an unsteady firing position.

One feature of the **SA80** which has gone down very well with British troops is the sling. This allows you to have both hands free, with the weapon secured in several different positions.

The Sling

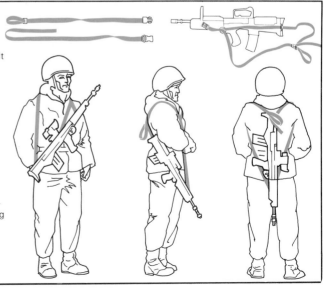

The SA80's sling allows the weapon to be secured to your body, leaving both hands free. It consists of two lengths of webbing; a longer piece with a female clip and a flat plastic loop attached, and a shorter piece with the male part of the clip at one end and a quick-release buckle and loop at the other end.

To position the SA80 across the chest, separate the two straps and slip the loop over your head, right arm and shoulder. The weapon will be suspended across your left shoulder and its position adjusted by pulling on the clear end of the longer strap. Tugging the quick release loop or releasing the clip will allow the weapon to be aimed.

Inside the SA80

Firing the new NATO 5.56-mm cartridge, the SA80 produces so little recoil that you can keep the target in your sights all the time. This is a great improvement over the SLR, which tends to veer off target with each round. It is exceptionally accurate at battlefield ranges and is capable of fully automatic fire.

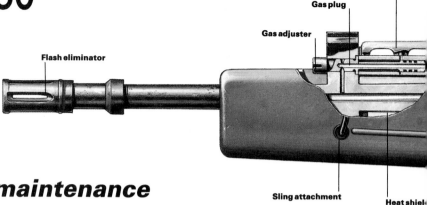

Gas cylinder
When a bullet is
of the gas produc
diverted along he
back the piston r

Handguard cover

Gas plug

Gas adjuster

Flash eliminator

Sling attachment

Heat shiel

Field stripping and maintenance

After firing 200 rounds, the SA80 should be stripped down and cleaned so that it will continue to function properly. Before commencing the field strip you must perform basic safety precautions: (1) release the safety catch; (2) set the change lever to 'R'; (3) cock the weapon, look inside and check that the chamber is clear; (4) let the working parts go forward, reapply safety catch and leave the dust cover open.

1 Take out the locking pins; first the rear one, then the front one. Once the rear pin is fully out it should be pushed in about 5mm so that its base is not showing. This stops the recoil spring assembly flying out when you remove the TMH (Trigger Mechanism Housing).

2 Keeping the body of the weapon upside down and horizontal, remove the TMH by extracting the front locking pin and pulling the TMH from the body, butt first.

3 Fully withdraw the rear locking pin and remove the recoil spring assembly, but do not separate the spring from the assembly.

4 Pull the cocking handle to the rear to unlock the bolt, raise the muzzle slightly and slide out the cocking handle and carrier.

5 Strip down the carrier and bolt: remove the firing-pin retaining pin from the carrier. This is very small, and in the field should be placed in a beret to stop it getting lost. Remove the firing pin.

6 Remove the bolt from the bolt carrier and place this with the firing pin and its retaining pin in your beret.

Because of its 'bullpup' design the SA80's empty cases are ejected from a port right opposite the firer's face, so it can only be fired right-handed. But in extensive tests with the new weapon left-handed soldiers have had little difficulty in adjusting to right-handed shooting.

Taking out the target

The SA80 is the first combat weapon to be issued to front-line troops with a telescopic sight as a standard fitting. The sight, known as SUSAT (Sight Unit, Small Arms, Trilux) gives a 4× magnification and comes fitted with a comfortable rubber eyepiece. Through this the shooter sees a pointer – dark in daylight, illuminated with the radioactive Trilux lamp in poor light – that he places against the target. The SUSAT sight gives the British infantryman a massive advantage over a conventionally-equipped enemy and lets him unleash a hail of accurate fire even in the worst combat conditions.

A selector lever set at R (for 'repetition') lets you fire the SA80 a shot at a time, while set at A ('automatic') the rifle will fire for as long as the trigger is pressed and there are rounds in the magazine. Which you use depends largely on the tactical circumstances but, unlike some, the British Army has a long tradition of marksmanship and economy of fire. Automatic fire will be reserved for the last stages of an assault or for house-to-house fighting.

Out of the SA80's business end comes a 5.56-mm round that's light enough for each man to carry a standard ration of eight 30-round magazines plus a bandolier of ammo. Light

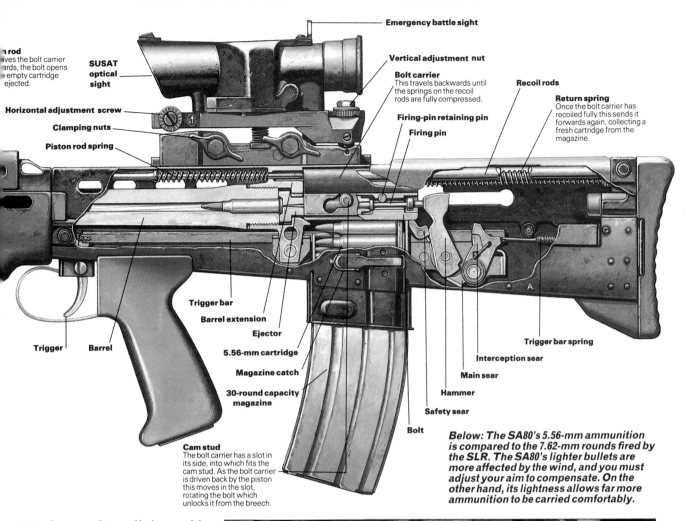

Emergency battle sight

n rod
ives the bolt carrier
ards, the bolt opens
e empty cartridge
ejected.

SUSAT optical sight

Horizontal adjustment screw

Clamping nuts

Piston rod spring

Vertical adjustment nut

Bolt carrier
This travels backwards until the springs on the recoil rods are fully compressed.

Firing-pin retaining pin

Firing pin

Recoil rods

Return spring
Once the bolt carrier has recoiled fully this sends it forwards again, collecting a fresh cartridge from the magazine.

Trigger bar

Barrel extension

Ejector

5.56-mm cartridge

Magazine catch

30-round capacity magazine

Trigger

Barrel

Cam stud
The bolt carrier has a slot in its side, into which fits the cam stud. As the bolt carrier is driven back by the piston this moves in the slot, rotating the bolt which unlocks it from the breech.

Bolt

Safety sear

Hammer

Main sear

Interception sear

Trigger bar spring

Below: The SA80's 5.56-mm ammunition is compared to the 7.62-mm rounds fired by the SLR. The SA80's lighter bullets are more affected by the wind, and you must adjust your aim to compensate. On the other hand, its lightness allows far more ammunition to be carried comfortably.

as it is, the round is still thoroughly effective at up to 600 metres — although in practice small-arms fire is rarely called for at ranges over 300 metres.

Currently, the SA80 is issued with magazines made for the US Army's M16. Although theoretically compatible these magazines are in fact ill-made and a constant cause of stoppage. Fortunately a custom-made magazine is on its way, though that may be little comfort to those who come under fire in the meantime.

The new ammo gives very little recoil, so the SA80 can be held on target

7 To strip the gas parts at the front of the SA80, lift the cover and pull the piston back so that the spring is depressed, and pull off the gas cylinder.

8 Pull out the piston and its spring. The spring stays on the piston, and should not be removed. Take out the gas plug by depressing and pushing it through its housing.

9 Carbon fouling is cleaned off the bolt with a nylon pad. With a little oil this will also remove rust but, like a pan scourer, should not be used on weapon parts coated with a protective finish.

Weapons and Equipment Guide

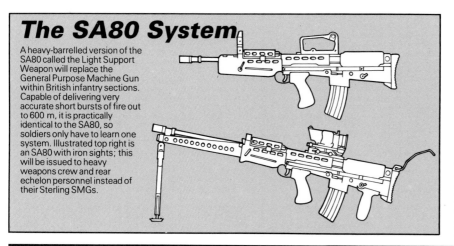

The SA80 System

A heavy-barrelled version of the SA80 called the Light Support Weapon will replace the General Purpose Machine Gun within British infantry sections. Capable of delivering very accurate short bursts of fire out to 600 m, it is practically identical to the SA80, so soldiers only have to learn one system. Illustrated top right is an SA80 with iron sights; this will be issued to heavy weapons crew and rear echelon personnel instead of their Sterling SMGs.

for continuous firing – whereas most assault rifles tend to jump off target with every shot and thump heavily into the shooter's shoulder. Wind does easily affect the flight of the bullet, however, so your aim has to compensate for this.

Three into one

The SA80 replaces three weapons in the infantry armoury: the SLR, the 9-mm Sterling submachine gun, and the 7.62-mm General Purpose Machine Gun. To take the GPMG's place there will be a version with a heavy barrel and bipod. Known as the Light Support Weapon, it is virtually

Battlefield Evaluation: comparing

5.56-mm SA80 Individual Weapon

Specification:
Cartridge: 5.56-mm NATO
Weight: 5 kg
Length: 785 mm
Cyclic rate of fire: 800 rounds per minute
Magazine: 30-round box
Effective range: 500 m

A complete weapons system replacing the British Army's rifles, LMGs and SMGs, the SA80 is arguably the finest service rifle available today. Short and handy, it is ideal both for urban combat and for the cramped interior of an APC. Its SUSAT sight is a great aid to accuracy and is especially valuable when shooting in poor light conditions.

Assessment
Reliability ★★★★★
Accuracy ★★★★★
Age ★
Worldwide users ★

The SA80 has proved itself a remarkably tough rifle in an extensive testing programme.

7.62-mm L1A1 Self-Loading Rifle

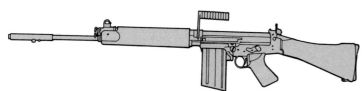

Specification
Cartridge: 7.62 mm ×51 NATO
Weight: 5 kg
Length: 1143 mm
Rate of fire: (single shot) 40 rounds per minute
Magazine: 20-round box
Effective range: 500 m

The British Army is one of about 50 armies to use a version of the Belgian FN FAL. In service for nearly 30 years, it has been obsolete for some time and many regiments have found teaching marksmanship with worn-out weapons to be an impossible task. Its 7.62-mm ammunition is unnecessarily powerful for the modern battlefield.

Assessment
Reliability ★★★
Accuracy ★★
Age ★★★★★
Worldwide users ★★★★★

Seen here in Northern Ireland, the SLR has been used all over the world by British soldiers.

5.56-mm AR-15 (M16) Rifle

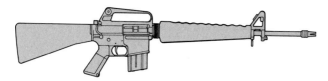

Specification: (M16A2)
Cartridge: 5.56 mm NATO
Weight: 4 kg
Length: 1000 mm
Cyclic rate of fire: 600 rounds per minute
Magazine: 20- or 30-round box
Effective range: 500 m

The M16 started the fashion for 5.56-mm ammunition and the latest model, the M16A2, is a substantial improvement over the original version used by US troops in Vietnam. Stronger and with better sights, full automatic fire has been replaced by a three-round burst option which gives three shots at a high rate for one pull of the trigger.

Assessment
Reliability ★★★★
Accuracy ★★★
Age ★★★★
Worldwide users ★★★★

The M16 has proved itself a good rifle after an uncertain beginning in Vietnam.

identical to the SA80, so soldiers will now need to be familiar with only one weapon instead of three, while the ammunition is interchangeable with all NATO small arms chambered for the new 5.56-mm cartridge. With his new rifle in his hands the British infantryman can easily outshoot any potential opponent.

Right: A soldier dives to the ground after running 100 yards to deliver 10 aimed shots at a target 200 yards away. British troops have found the SA80 to be tough, accurate and reliable.

the SA80 with its rivals.

7.62-mm Kalashnikov AKM Rifle

Specification
Cartridge: 7.62 mm ×39
Weight: 3.15 kg
Length: 876 mm
Cyclic rate of fire: 600 rounds per minute
Magazine: 30-round box
Effective range: 400 m

Assessment:
Reliability	★★★★
Accuracy	★★★
Age	★★★★★
Worldwide users	★★★★★

The AK series of assault rifles are brutally simple pieces of kit, and very reliable.

...e modernised version of the original AK-47, the AKM is now being replaced in ...arsaw Pact service but vast numbers remain operational all over the world. Very ...mple and easy to operate, the AKM is ideal for third-world guerrillas. Its only real ...sadvantage is the change lever, which makes a resounding click and is tricky to ...ove while wearing Arctic mittens.

...MI Galil Assault Rifle

Specification: (7.62-mm assault rifle)
Cartridge: 7.62-mm NATO
Weight: 4.9 kg
Length: 1050 mm
Rate of fire: 600 rounds per minute
Magazine: 25-round box
Effective range: 500 m

Assessment
Reliability	★★★★
Accuracy	★★★★
Age	★★
Worldwide users	★★

The Israelis value rugged simplicity too, and the Galil follows the AK tradition.

...rael's first home-produced rifle, the Galil is produced in two models: one firing ...ll-power 7.62-mm NATO ammunition, and one firing 5.56-mm. Closely based on ...e AK series, the Galil has one feature that shows good appreciation of soldiers' ...se of firearms; it has a built-in bottle opener.

...56-mm FA MAS Rifle

Specification:
Cartridge: 5.56-mm ×45
Weight: 4.5 kg
Length: 757 mm
Cyclic rate of fire: 900-1000 rounds per minute
Magazine: 25-round box
Effective range: 400 m

Assessment
Reliability	★★★
Accuracy	★★★
Age	★
Worldwide users	★

The FA MAS is the only other 'bullpup' rifle to have been adopted apart from the SA80.

...bullpup design like the SA80, the French FA MAS can be set to eject spent cases ... each side, although this is a fiddly job. Its phenomenal rate of fire will empty a ...5-round magazine in 1½ seconds, and it takes practice to control.

Riding the Devil's Chariot

Although large and perhaps a little unwieldy, the Mi-24 'Hind' is the undisputed king of the battlefield helicopters. It is fast, heavily-armed and well-armoured, with sophisticated avionics systems to ensure that it can deliver its weapons with deadly accuracy. Both 'Hind' and its crews have been honed in combat in the rugged mountains of Afghanistan, where it is known to the Mujahideen as the 'Devil's Chariot'.

Worldwide weapon

'Hind' has been widely exported to a wide range of Soviet client states, and is an important front-line aircraft in most of the world's trouble spots. Although not invulnerable to intensive ground fire, it has impressed most of those who have come up against it with its toughness and firepower. 'Hind' has been used in anger by Iraq during the ongoing Gulf War with Iran, by Angola against the South African-backed UNITA guerillas and by Nicaragua against rebel right-wing Contra guerillas, as well as by the

The 'Hind' has been widely exported to client states of the Soviet Union. Among the most important users is India.

Soviet and Afghan air forces in Afghanistan.

This type of Third World counter-insurgency fighting, however, does not give a true idea of the role for which 'Hind' was designed. The Soviet Union realised the military potential of the helicopter at a relatively early stage, seeing beyond the limited roles asigned to British, French and American helicopters in Malaya, Cyprus, Algeria and Vietnam.

The helicopter is inherently vulner-

The distinctive shape of the 'Devil's Chariot' menaces all who see it. Despite its fearsome reputation, it is vulnerable due to its large size and lack of manoeuvrability.

able over a modern battlefield, but Soviet willingness to accept heavy losses allowed their air force planners to view the helicopter virtually as an airborne tank, being heavily armed and yet able to move swiftly over the battlefield, regardless of terrain.

While NATO has never been keen

to commit its transport helicopters too far forward, too close to the FEBA (Forward Edge of Battle Area), the Soviet Union has a tradition of arming its utility and support helicopters with guns and rocket pods to allow them to be used in a more direct assault transport role even in the hostile European environment.

By the mid-1960s the Soviet Union was able to draw up a requirement for a new, dedicated assault helicopter able to carry an eight-man infantry or anti-tank squad, well-armoured and packing the biggest possible punch to allow offensive operations over enemy territory. Roles for the new helicopter included anti-armour, anti-helicopter, transport, transport helicopter escort and direct assault, and prototypes of the new machine flew in 1970.

'Hinds' have played a large part in the counter-insurgency war in Afghanistan. This Afghan air force 'Hind-D' carries UV-32-57 rocket pods, which are sometimes used with chemical warheads.

With heavy firepower and the ability to carry small parties of specialist troops, the Mi-24 is a perfect vehicle for supporting amphibious operations. These two are on exercise in the Baltic.

The 'Hind' is a fearsome battlefield weapon, able to destroy vehicles and insert troops. Often the two tasks are combined, using the helicopter's awesome firepower to 'sanitise' a landing zone before dropping troops into it.

The Mi-24 is loosely based on the Mi-8 'Hip' transport helicopter, although it has more powerful engines and smaller rotor blades. The whole fuselage was redesigned to give a smaller cabin and a slimmer cross-section. The four-man crew, comprising two pilots, a navigator and a gunner, sit under a streamlined canopy, with the pilots to the rear. Early 'Hinds' set an impressive number of world speed records, and the type was in front line service by 1974, receiving the NATO code-name 'Hind-A'.

Heavy armour

'Hind-A' was an impressive machine by any standards, with its nose-mounted 12.7-mm cannon, underwing rocket pods and radio-guided AT-2 'Swatter' anti-tank mis-

Inside the 'Hind

siles and heavy armour, but it was soon superseded by the even more capable 'Hind-D'. This new version was a dedicated gunship, with a completely new forward fuselage housing a new two-man cockpit and a baffling array of sophisticated sensors. A new four-barrel Gatling-type 12.7 mm rotary cannon was installed in a chin-mounted turret, and new low-light television, radar, forward-looking infra-red and laser sensors were also fitted.

Far-reaching missile

The laser, mounted on the port wingtip, was associated with the new AT-6 'Spiral' laser guided, tube-launched anti-tank missile. 'Spiral' is believed to have an effective range of up to 5000 metres, making it considerably 'further-reaching' than the Hughes TOW, its closest Western equivalent. This long range allows 'Hind-D' to engage tanks while remaining well beyond the effective

Field maintenance is undertaken rapidly, thanks to easy access to vital components via fold-down doors. The size of the weapons pylons is readily apparent here.

range of their armament. 'Hind-D' was also structurally strengthened, with stronger rotor blades and increased titanium content in the airframe.

'Hind-D' is now an important part of Soviet Frontal Aviation, and would be extensively used in the intensive, co-ordinated fixed-wing and rotary-wing air operations that would accompany any thrust by the ground forces. The main aims of such Soviet air operations would include the destruction of enemy aircraft and helicopters, and their crews, on the ground or in the air.

Two Czech air force machines stay below the treeline during a realistic exercise of wartime operations.

Cockpits
Pilot and gunner sit in separate cockpits, with the pilot raised to the rear. Although the canopies are not bullet-proof, the windscreens are. The optically-flat screen is made up of glass and plastic sandwiches to withstand 23-mm shell hits.

Air-data probe
These vanes measure drift, yaw and airspeed, especially at low speeds or in the hover. The information is fed to an onboard computer for accurate weapons delivery.

Gun
This 'Hind-E' version has a 12.7-mm rapid fire four-barrelled cannon in the nose turret. Able to traverse through a wide angle in both elevation and azimuth, the gun is slaved to the undernose sensors for accuracy.

Tactical missiles, command, control, communications and intelligence facilities, nuclear warheads, fuel dumps, ammunition supplies and airfields would also form important priority targets.

Rapid penetration

The 'Hind' would also be used in support of Operational Manoeuvre Groups, formations of at least divisional strength whose purpose is rapidly to penetrate enemy defences and operate deep in his rear areas for a limited period.

The Mi-24 'Hind' would rarely operate independently, usually being used in conjunction with fixed-wing close-support aircraft. Tactics involving the co-ordinated use of fast-jets and 'Hinds' have been developed and refined during the long war in Afghanistan, and the Sukhoi Su-25 'Frog-

Rotor blades
The forged titanium rotor hub and five high-tensile steel rotor blades are designed to take hits from 23-mm cannon and continue functioning.

Infra-red countermeasures
On either side of the engines are mounted exhaust heat suppressors to dissipate infra-red energy. The 'lighthouse' type fairing behind the engines is an infra-red countermeasures emitter, which breaks the lock-on gained by heat-seeking missiles.

Undernose sensors
On the left under the nose is a fairing for low light level TV and possibly forward-looking infra-red, both of which give adverse weather and night capability. In this pod to starboard is a target detection and ranging radar.

Cabin
The internal cabin can take eight fully-equipped troops for the insertion role, using its firepower to clear defences before dropping the troops. Reload missiles are also carried in the cabin.

Rockets
The most common rocket pods carried by the Mi-24 are the UV-32-57 unit, carrying 32 57-mm unguided rockets. Rails at the end of the stub pylons mount AT-6 'Spiral' anti-tank missiles.

foot' has emerged as a particularly useful complement to the 'Hind', acting as an escort and defence suppression aircraft. The 'Frogfoot', with its better endurance and payload, can loiter in the area, and is less vulnerable than the 'Hind'. The Su-25 is slow enough to be able to take in the tactical environment, and yet fast and agile enough to be a difficult target for enemy anti-aircraft artillery.

Major offensive

Mi-24s usually operate in flights of four, sub-divided into pairs for mutual support. The two flights can then make co-ordinated attacks from different directions, or one flight can attack while the other draws enemy fire. Like Western helicopters the Mi-24s generally transit to their targets flying close to the ground ('nap of earth') making maximum use of ter-

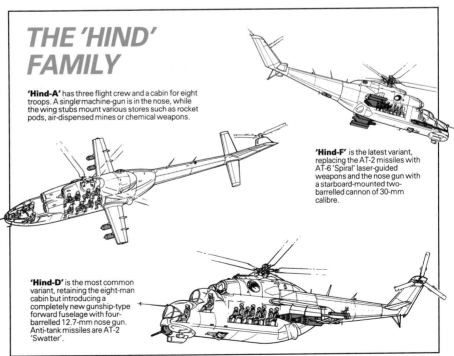

THE 'HIND' FAMILY

'Hind-A' has three flight crew and a cabin for eight troops. A single machine-gun is in the nose, while the wing stubs mount various stores such as rocket pods, air-dispensed mines or chemical weapons.

'Hind-F' is the latest variant, replacing the AT-2 missiles with AT-6 'Spiral' laser-guided weapons and the nose gun with a starboard-mounted two-barrelled cannon of 30-mm calibre.

'Hind-D' is the most common variant, retaining the eight-man cabin but introducing a completely new gunship-type forward fuselage with four-barrelled 12.7-mm nose gun. Anti-tank missiles are AT-2 'Swatter'.

217

rain cover to avoid exposure to enemy radar.

Where defensive fire is light the 'Hind' can make a diving attack from about 1,000 metres, allowing it to deliver its weapon load with extreme accuracy before breaking into evasive terrain-hugging flight. This sort of attack profile is ideally suited to the delivery of free-fall bombs, unguided rockets, or for strafe attacks using the cannon.

The latest major Mi-24 variant, dubbed 'Hind-F' by NATO, has its chin-turret mounted 12.7-mm cannon re-

Primary anti-armour weapon of the 'Hind-D' is the AT-2 Swatter, which incorporates tracking flares.

Battlefield Evaluation: comparing

Mil Mi-24 'Hind-D'

The Mi-24 is fast and heavily-armoured, although its sheer size makes it a little unwieldy. 'Hind' can carry a wide range of ordnance, including guided missiles, rocket pods and freefall bombs as well as various types of chemical weapon. 'Hind-D' and 'Hind-E' have a remote-controlled four-barrel 12.7-mm cannon in an undernose turret, while 'Hind-F' has a fixed twin-barrelled 30-mm cannon on the fuselage side.

Specification:
Length overall: 21.50 m
Rotor diameter: 17.0 m
Maximum cruising speed: 159 kts
Radius: 160 km
Standard weapon load: four UV-32-57 rocket pods; four AT-2 'Sagger' missiles; one four-barrel 12.7-mm cannon

Assessment
Defensive
   systems/armour ★★★★★
Firepower   ★★★★
Versatility   ★★★
Worldwide users   ★★★★

The 'Hind' is fitted with many countermeasures, yet its size still makes it an inviting target.

Mil Mi-8 'Hip-E'

'Hip-E' is the world's most heavily-armed helicopter, able to carry six UV-32-57 rocket pods with a total of 192 unguided 57-mm rockets, up to four AT-2 'Swatter' or six AT-3 'Sagger' anti tank guided missiles, and a flexibly-mounted 12.7-mm machine-gun in the nose. The 'Hip-E' usually operates in the assault transport role, escorted by Mi-24 'Hind' gunships, but can be used as an independent dedicated attack helicopter.

Specification:
Length overall: 25.24 m
Rotor diameter: 21.29 m
Maximum cruising speed: 122 kts
Radius: 445 km
Standard weapon load: six UV-32-57 rocket pods; four AT-2 'Sagger' missiles; one nose-mounted 12.7-mm machine-gun

Assessment
Defensive
   systems/armour ★★★
Firepower   ★★★★★
Versatility   ★★★★★
Worldwide users   ★★★★★

Workhorse of the WarPac assault fleets, the Mi-8 can also be used to launch heavy rocket attacks.

Mil Mi-28 'Havoc'

'Havoc' is a new, purpose-designed, dedicated attack helicopter which is now being deployed with Soviet Frontal Aviation. The aircraft is believed to use two Isotov TV3-117 turboshaft engines as fitted to the 'Hind' and 'Hip', but probably with a new rotor system. The aircraft is as heavily armed as the 'Hind' but employs a slimmer fuselage with no cabin, being similar in layout to the AH-64 Apache.

Specification:
(estimated)
Length overall: (excluding rotors) 17.40 m
Rotor diameter: 17.00 m
Maximum cruising speed: 162 kts
Radius: 240 km
Probable weapon load: various rocket pods; guided anti-tank missiles

Assessment
Defensive
   systems/armour ★★★★★
Firepower   ★★★★★
Versatility   ★★
Worldwide users   ★

A dedicated gunship, the Mi-28 is still a large target despite considerable improvements in speed and agility.

placed by a twin-barrelled weapon fixed to the starboard forward fuselage. This weapon is thought to be of 23-mm calibre, with improved range and firepower.

The standard S-5 57-mm rocket has a HEAT shaped-charge warhead capable of penetrating 220-mm of armour and a range in excess of 1,200 metres. Rockets, cannon or anti-tank guided missiles can be fired while the helicopter is hovering, popping up from behind cover to fire.

The 'Hind' will be an important element in any Soviet attack, helping to achieve a swift, relentless advance. Lessons learned in Afghanistan are continually being applied in Europe, with successful pilots being given command of front-line European squadrons, and with new equipment in the form of infra-red jammers and exhaust suppressors being fitted to the 'Hind' fleet.

The success of the 'Hind' has led to the development of a new generation of attack helicopters, dedicated gunships with no troop-carrying capability but with superb manoeuvrability, thick armour and sophisticated weapons such as the Mi-28 'Havoc' and Kamov 'Hokum'.

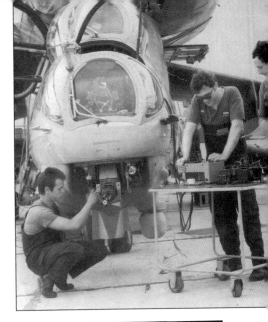

Ground crew service the 'Hind's' nose gun. Ammunition is loaded through the doors immediately above it.

the 'Hind' with its rivals

McDonnell Douglas AH-64 Apache

The Apache is fast and very agile, and is packed with sophisticated sensors and advanced avionics which enable it to find and attack targets with extreme accuracy in all weathers. Despite its rugged structure the aircraft has proved troublesome in service, with numerous groundings due to technical problems. Lack of a roof- or mast-mounted sight is also a major disadvantage.

Specification:
Length overall: 17.76 m
Rotor diameter: 14.63 m
Maximum cruising speed: 155 kts
Radius: 482 km
Probable weapon load: M230 30-mm Chain Gun; 16 Rockwell Hellfire anti-tank missiles

Assessment
Defensive systems/armour	*****
Firepower	****
Versatility	***
Worldwide users	*

Designed for all-weather operations, the Apache can make mincemeat of enemy armour without ever being seen.

Kamov-Ka 'Hokum'

Few details are available concerning the 'Hokum', which first flew in 1984 and which will shortly be entering service. It is fitted with contra-rotating coaxial rotors and is thought to be outstandingly manoeuvrable. It will serve in both the attack and the air-to-air anti-helicopter roles. The West has no counterpart to this versatile and hard-hitting helicopter.

Specification:
(estimated)
Length overall: (excluding rotors, probe and gun) 13.5 m
Rotor diameter: 15.0 m
Maximum cruising speed: 189 kts
Radius: 250 km
Probable weapon load: two rocket pods and four missiles

Assessment
Defensive systems/armour	***
Firepower	***
Versatility	**
Worldwide users	*

In addition to its anti-armour role, the incredibly agile 'Hokum' can take on enemy helicopters.

Westland Lynx AH.Mk1

The Lynx is fast, highly manoeuvrable and well equipped, but with only eight TOW missiles it lacks combat persistence. It is felt by many to be unduly fragile, and it is certainly rather noisy. Night and all-weather capability is to be added to the roof-mounted sight, and a fire-and-forget missile (such as the Rockwell Hellfire). These improvements will make the Lynx an even more useful tool.

Specification:
Length overall: 15.16 m
Rotor diameter: 12.80 m
Maximum cruising speed: 140 kts
Radius: 180 km
Probable weapon load: eight Hughes TOW missiles

Assessment
Defensive systems/armour	*
Firepower	**
Versatility	****
Worldwide users	*

Speed, firepower, manoeuvrability and versatility make the Lynx perhaps the best all-round battlefield helicopter.

A-10: Warthog Warrior

There can be few more ugly flying machines than the Fairchild A-10, yet its uncompromising lines can be a thing of beauty to a NATO soldier pinned down by enemy armour. Called Thunderbolt II by its makers and the US Air Force, it is known as 'Warthog' to all its friends, a more than apt epithet for this mean, sturdy and punchy aircraft.

Its ugliness has purpose: survivability over the battlefield. The giant engines are mounted in 'dustbins' high over the mid-rear fuselage, where their hot exhausts are shielded from heat-seeking missiles by wings, tail and tailplane. There are two fins to

A pair of A-10s demonstrate their agility with a rapid break. A-10s are ready to deploy to troubled areas around the world, carrying large ferry tanks, as here, to extend their range.

A Warthog driver mounts his steed by the integral ladder which pulls out of the aircraft. Standard flying kit is worn, with the occasional addition of rubber 'poopy' suits for overwater operations; these insulate the pilot against cold in the event of ditching.

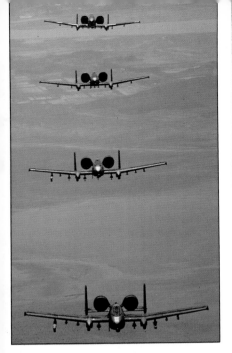

Above: Four A-10s transit at medium altitude. The engines are mounted so that their exhausts are shielded from heat-seeking missiles.

shield the engines, and to provide stability even if one gets shot away. The long wings are incredibly strong, able to take a large number of hits from ground fire and haul a heavy offensive load.

In the firing line

Load control surfaces give phenomenal agility, enabling the A-10 to dodge and weave through a wall of flak. Elsewhere on the aircraft are heavy armour 'bathtubs' to protect the pilot and ammunition drum from cannon rounds. All these protective measures are necessary, for the 'Warthog' is expected to fly low and slow in the teeth of WarPac fire, right over the fiercest fighting.

The A-10 was designed to take on Viet Cong guerrillas in the steamy jungles of Vietnam, but by the time it was ready for service the war was long over. A new role emerged for the aircraft, namely that of anti-tank operations, and it has pursued this with vigour. Currently based in Korea, Alaska and Europe in addition to the United States, the 'Warthog' can expect to be in the front line in any future conflict, confronting WarPac armoured formations as they attempt to smash through Western defences.

Training for war

In Europe the aircraft are based in England, but forward-deploy to West German bases, where they train for a Central Front war. Individual pilots fly over set pieces of terrain so that they know the likely 'killing grounds', where tanks congregate in choke points. They also practise operating

Ammunition for the GAU-8/A cannon is loaded into an A-10. The ammunition is housed in a titanium armour bath to protect it from stray hits.

from autobahns and service stations, which they would use if their airfields were attacked.

Missions are flown at very low level, the pilots taking full advantage of terrain features to mask the aircraft's approach to the target and to shield it from enemy fire. Low for an

Among the areas of the world patrolled by A-10s, the most inhospitable is Alaska. This pair carries practice bombs over the tundra.

The A-10's cockpit is sparse in contrast with other jet fighters, uncluttered by sophisticated avionics. The screen on the right is for launching Maverick missiles.

A-10 pilot means low, jinking the aircraft and threading it down seemingly impossible valleys, often below the height of trees. Nevertheless, the 'Warthog' is very slow, and whenever it leaves the protection of the terrain it is extremely vulnerable to attack from the ground. Additional protection is

Cockpit armour

The A-10 has many features designed for increased survivability. Obviously the most important 'component' of the aircraft is the pilot, and he is afforded considerable protection by being seated in a titanium 'bathtub', which can absorb hits of up to 23-mm calibre. The windscreen and canopy are made of toughened Perspex to give all-round protection.

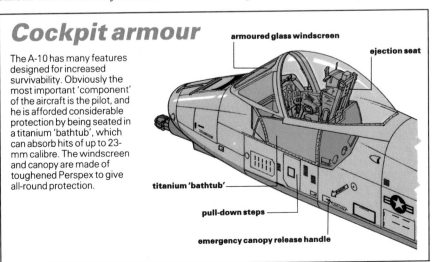

armoured glass windscreen
ejection seat
titanium 'bathtub'
pull-down steps
emergency canopy release handle

Inside the A-10

The A-10 has been designed to cover all the shortfalls of operations over the battlefield. Survivability and heavy armament are the primary concerns of its design.

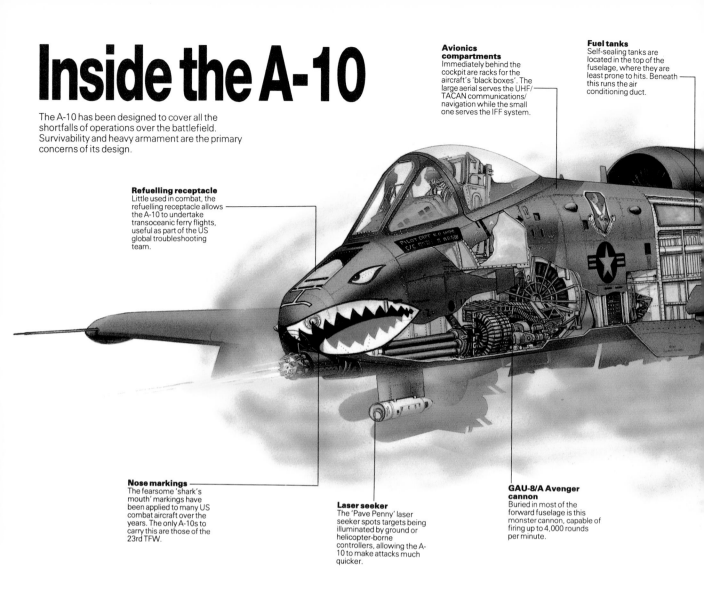

Avionics compartments
Immediately behind the cockpit are racks for the aircraft's 'black boxes'. The large aerial serves the UHF/TACAN communications/navigation while the small one serves the IFF system.

Fuel tanks
Self-sealing tanks are located in the top of the fuselage, where they are least prone to hits. Beneath this runs the air conditioning duct.

Refuelling receptacle
Little used in combat, the refuelling receptacle allows the A-10 to undertake transoceanic ferry flights, useful as part of the US global troubleshooting team.

Nose markings
The fearsome 'shark's mouth' markings have been applied to many US combat aircraft over the years. The only A-10s to carry this are those of the 23rd TFW.

Laser seeker
The 'Pave Penny' laser seeker spots targets being illuminated by ground or helicopter-borne controllers, allowing the A-10 to make attacks much quicker.

GAU-8/A Avenger cannon
Buried in most of the forward fuselage is this monster cannon, capable of firing up to 4,000 rounds per minute.

afforded by flares and chaff which decoy heat-seeking and radar-homing missiles.

'Warthogs' fly usually in pairs, with one pair engaging the enemy while another loiters to the rear of the battle-zone, waiting to streak into action when the initial attack has been completed. When called into the battle area, the A-10s hit the deck and fly as low as possible towards their operational area, using terrain masking to the full to shield their approach.

Most operations take place in concert with a forward air controller (FAC), who is either in or beyond the forward line of troops, or in a light scout helicopter. The FAC spots targets for the A-10 and any gunship helicopters working the area, and then directs the attackers towards them. Often he has a laser designator with which he 'spots' the target.

'Pop-up' manoeuvre

Close to the target the A-10 pulls up to acquire it, either visually or by picking up the reflected laser signal from the FAC. Hanging down from the A-10's nose is a 'Pave Penny' seeker to perform this job. During the 'pop-up' manoeuvre the A-10 is vulnerable to enemy fire, and the pilot punches out chaff and flare to distract missiles. Only jinking manoeuvres can deter guns.

Once the target has been acquired, the A-10 aims its weapons and fires, before screaming back down to the safety of ultra low level. The pilot flies low out of the battlezone until he

GAU-8/A ammunition

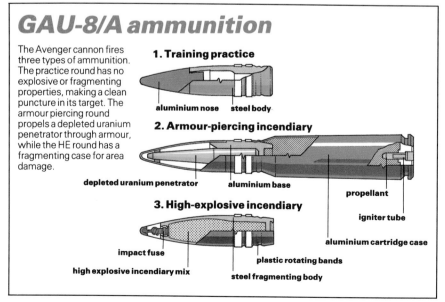

The Avenger cannon fires three types of ammunition. The practice round has no explosive or fragmenting properties, making a clean puncture in its target. The armour piercing round propels a depleted uranium penetrator through armour, while the HE round has a fragmenting case for area damage.

1. Training practice

aluminium nose   steel body

2. Armour-piercing incendiary

depleted uranium penetrator   aluminium base   propellant   igniter tube   aluminium cartridge case

3. High-explosive incendiary

impact fuse   high explosive incendiary mix   plastic rotating bands   steel fragmenting body

Fairchild A-10

Cooling system
This box between the engines contains the inlet and exhaust for the aircraft's cooling system.

Engines
These are set in their distinctive position to give them maximum shielding from heat-seeking missiles, the exhaust being shrouded by the fins or wings from most angles.

Tail markings
In common with most USAF tactical aircraft, this A-10 wears the Wing letters (23rd Tactical Fighter Wing, England AFB, Louisiana) and a coloured fin-stripe denoting the squadron (75th Tactical Fighter Squadron). The large shield is that of Tactical Air Command.

Wings
Immensely strong, the wings have flaps and slats to improve low-speed performance. The ailerons can split in two to form divebrakes.

Maverick missiles
Principal weapon of the A-10 is the Maverick missile, usually carried in pairs or trios under each wing.

ECM pod
Most USAF tactical aircraft now carry the ALQ-131 pod to protect them from enemy radar-guided missiles.

...ats
...all slats on the centre ...ng section aid the low- ...eed handling qualities of ...A-10.

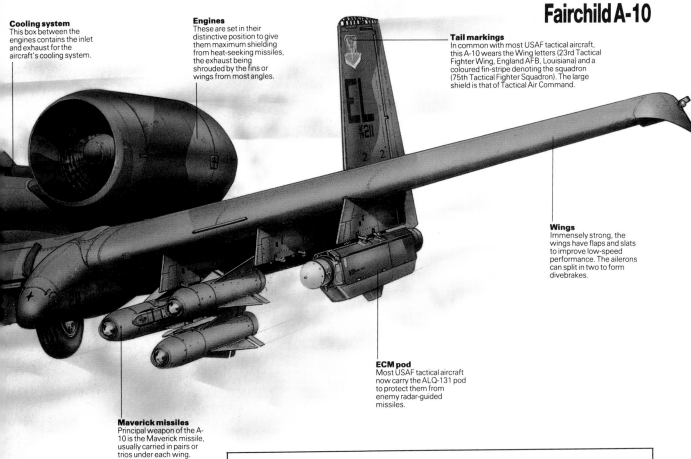

Maverick missile on launcher

This cutaway shows the main components of the Maverick missile. The TV seeker, electronics and control fins aim the missile to its target and the rocket motor powers the missile. In the centre is a shaped-charge warhead, which fires a jet of molten metal through armour or concrete defences.

missile/launcher umbilical connector
launcher/aircraft electrical connector
standard lugs for loading
launcher electronics unit
launch rails
TV seeker
missile electronics
shaped charge warhead
safe, arm and fuse
battery
solid rocket motor
blast tube
gas bottle and pump
flight control surfaces

---

reaches the safety of the rear area. If the A-10 still has weapons aboard and plenty of fuel, it can loiter to await another call to action, either flying orbits or ground-loitering, waiting on a stretch of road with the auxiliary power unit running to provide power for an instant start-up and return to action. When the aircraft is low on fuel or weapons it returns to its base, where it can be rearmed and refuelled in minutes for another four-hour mission.

Weapons selection

The 'Warthog' packs a heavy punch against enemy armour, with several weapon systems available. At the heart of the aircraft is the fearsome GAU-8/A Avenger 30-mm cannon. This seven-barrelled monstrosity fires massive rounds with depleted (non-radioactive) uranium cores for armour penetration, turning the A-10 into something of a flying can-opener.

Blessed with enormous range, the Avenger is still considered a close-in weapon, and in today's combat environment the prime weapon for anti-armour work is the Maverick missile. This has a seeker head in the nose that can be locked on to a chosen target by the pilot. Once the image is in the missile's memory, it can be fired and forgotten, allowing the pilot to escape out of the lethal area at altitude to the safety of the trees.

Meanwhile the missile has the target squarely in its own sights, and aims itself to an almost certain dead hit. The Maverick is available in three versions: one has a TV seeker for daytime operations, one has an infra-red sensor which presents a heat image of the target area, and one has a laser seeker to home in on the reflected laser beam from the FAC.

Other weapons are used less by the A-10, but can be of use in areas of low density defences. These include iron bombs, cluster bombs and rockets. In a departure from their anti-armour role, the A-10 can turn its mammoth gun against enemy helicopters, with disastrous results for anything in the way. Although not a fast aircraft, the A-10 itself is extremely difficult to shoot down thanks to its astonishing agility.

'Warthogs' have been the centre of a long and heated debate as to whether

The A-10 can operate from semi-prepared surfaces such as motorways. In wartime these could be used if the Warthog's airfield was put out of action.

Battlefield Evaluation: comparing

Fairchild A-10A Thunderbolt II

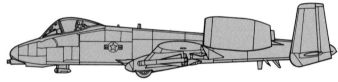

Fairchild A-10s serve with US Air Force units in Korea, United Kingdom and Germany, in addition to US-based units. Avionics are kept to a minimum, with only an inertial navigation system and head-up display to aid the pilot. Due to be replaced by the A-16, the A-10's main attributes are manoeuvrability and survivability.

Specification:
Length overall: 16.26 m
Wing span: 17.53 m
Maximum speed at sea level: 381 kts
Combat radius lo-lo-lo: 463 km (1.7 hours loiter)
Maximum external weapon load: 7257 kg
Take-off distance: 1,220 m (with max load)

Assessment
Manoeuvrability ★★★★★
Rough field capability ★★★
Versatility ★★★
Robustness ★★★★★
Worldwide users ★★★★★

The A-10 has strength and firepower in abundance, but is sorely lacking in speed.

Vought A-7 Corsair II

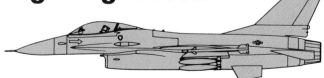

Commonly called the 'Sluf' (short little ugly fella), the A-7 was the A-10's predecessor in the close-air support role. Able to lift a large weapon load, the Corsair II is fast and agile, yet not as survivable over the battlefield. Many still serve with US Air National Guard units which would reinforce the current A-10 units in time of war. Small numbers also serve with Greece and Portugal, while it is still a major type in US Navy service.

Specification:
Length overall: 14.06 m
Wing span: 11.81 m
Maximum speed at sea level: 606 kts
Combat radius lo-lo-lo: 1432 km
Maximum external weapon load: 9072 kg
Take-off distance: 1,524 m (with max load)

Assessment
Manoeuvrability ★★
Rough field capability ★
Versatility ★★★★
Robustness ★★
Worldwide users ★★★

Preceding the A-10 with USAF units, the A-7 requires long runways, but carries a very large warload.

General Dynamics A-16 Fighting Falcon

The US Air Force has chosen an attack version of the tried and trusted F-16 fighter to take over from the A-10 during the 1990s to perform the battlefield attack role. To do this it will bring speed, better adverse weather capability and better countermeasures. Disadvantages will be the need for prepared runways and an inability to take much punishment from groundfire.

Specification:
Length overall: 15.01 m
Wing span: 10.01 m
Maximum speed at sea level: 793 kts
Combat radius lo-lo-lo: 547 km
Maximum external weapon load: 5443 kg
Take-off distance: 365 m

Assessment
Manoeuvrability ★★★★★
Rough field capability ★★
Versatility ★★★
Robustness ★★
Worldwide users ★

This is an F-16, already used in large numbers for the close support role. The A-16 will introduce even greater capability.

they can survive in a real war. Despite the inbuilt survivability measures, the problem of their slow speed is likely to lead to their demise. USAF plans call for an attack model of the General Dynamics F-16 (designated A-16) to take over the A-10's role, with the 'Warthogs' moving to FAC duties as OA-10s. Nevertheless, they have proved popular to their crews, and these men have no doubts as to their own survivability in the rough, tough, low and slow 'Warthog'.

Few modern warplanes can match the agility and low flying ability of the A-10. This Maverick-toting A-10 pulls up hard during a training sortie.

the A-10 with its rivals

British Aerospace Harrier GR.Mk 3

One of the most capable battlefield types, the Harrier is blessed with agility, speed and of course the ability to operate from truly dispersed sites hidden in the countryside. Improvements in avionics and countermeasures have enabled it to perform better in today's combat environment. Its major drawback is its lack of range.

Specification:
Length overall: 14.27 m
Wing span: 7.70 m
Maximum speed at sea level: 634 kts
Combat radius lo-lo-lo: 370 km (with external load)
Maximum external weapon load: 3630 kg
Take-off distance: vertical, or up to 300 metres

Assessment
Manoeuvrability ★★★★★
Rough field capability ★★★★★
Versatility ★★★★★
Robustness ★★
Worldwide users ★★

The Harrier's ability to fight from hidden bases makes up for lack of warload and overall performance.

Sukhoi Su-17 'Fitter'

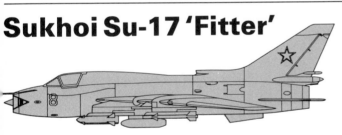

One of the major types to be encountered in the WarPac inventory is the various 'swing-wing' variants of the 'Fitter' family, which are fast, tough and punchy aircraft, although lacking in range and weapon load. These disadvantages have been eased in the 'Fitter-K' version, with leaner-burning engine. More modern avionics make this variant more accurate in the battlefield attack role.

Specification:
Length overall: 19.20 m
Wing span: 14.00 m (spread)
Maximum speed at sea level: (estimated) 695 kts
Combat radius lo-lo-lo: (estimated) 360 km
Maximum external weapon load: 3000 kg
Take-off distance: (clean) 610 m

Assessment
Manoeuvrability ★★★
Rough field capability ★★★
Versatility ★★★
Robustness ★★★★
Worldwide users ★★★★★

The big Sukhois will be a major force over any future battlefield, wielding good loads at fast speed.

Sukhoi Su-25 'Frogfoot'

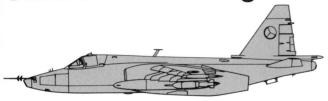

Development of the Su-25 was spurred by the A-10, but it is considerably faster, rendering it less vulnerable. Manoeuvrability is not quite as great, but its countermeasures fit is appreciably better. Being employed by large numbers by the Soviet Union and some of its allies, the 'Frogfoot' will be used on a similar role as the A-10: that of killing tanks on the battlefield.

Specification:
Length overall: 14.50 m
Wing span: 15.50 m
Maximum speed at sea level: (estimated) 475 kts
Combat radius lo-lo-lo: (estimated) 544 km
Maximum external weapon load: (estimated) 4000 kg
Take-off distance: (clean) 472 m

Assessment
Manoeuvrability ★★★★
Rough field capability ★★★★
Versatility ★
Robustness ★★★★
Worldwide users ★★★

The 'Frogfoot' is a direct Soviet answer to the A-10, but is faster at the expense of some agility.

Making Fire

Fire can be your best friend. It keeps you warm and dries your clothes; it cooks your food and purifies your water. But it can be your worst enemy, too. In enemy-held territory it can give away your position quicker than anything else. And a major burn is a dreadful wound, causing massive fluid loss and leaving you open to infection. This section of the survival course is devoted to fire: how to start it, control it and use in the most efficient way.

You have to bring three things together to make fire – fuel, heat and oxygen. Take away any one of these, and the fire goes out.

About a fifth of all the air around us is oxygen. All you have to do is make sure that there is free passage of air around – and especially up through – the fire.

Heat – the heat to start the fire – you have to provide. Friction in one form or another is the usual way, but you can use the rays of the sun, and perhaps even electricity, in its place.

You have to provide fuel in three quite different forms – **tinder**, to catch the spark; **kindling**, to set a flame; and the **fuel** itself, to keep the fire going.

Most fuel will not burn when it's wet. The water surrounds it and cuts off the air supply. Non-porous fuels like coal will burn when they are wet, however, and liquid fuels like oil, kerosene and petrol are completely unaffected by water.

Keep the fuel dry

But in most parts of the world it's wood and vegetable matter that you'll be burning, and this you must keep dry. Gathering and storing fuel for the fire is a very good example of how forward thinking pays dividends. But there is always something you can do to make a fire, even if you're shivering to death in a freezing rainstorm and the matches are soaked through.

Look for:
1 A sheltered place to build the fire.
2 Old, dead wood.
3 Kindling.
4 Tinder.

Take these tasks one at a time. Look for a rock overhang on the lee side of a hill or outcrop; or a low fallen branch or a fallen tree. At this stage you're looking for protection for the fire, not shelter for yourself.

The difference between warm, dry comfort and freezing, wet misery is a little knowledge and skill and a handful of basic materials. So learn the skills and get that fire going as soon as you basha down for the night.

Making a simple fire and oven

1 Scrape a small pit of about 60×60×60 cm with an extra gap at one end so that you can insert your food for cooking. Line the bottom and sides with stones the size of your fist.

2 Gather your firemaking materials together: tinder to catch the spark, kindling to get the fire under way, and fuel to keep it going.

3 If it's a bright day focus the rays of the sun through a magnifying lens – perhaps a pair of glasses – and onto the tinder. Hold it steady and you'll soon get a flame.

4 If you've got a 'flint and steel', strike a few sparks onto the tinder. This thistledown burst into flames immediately, but lint or cotton fluff would work just as well.

5 Carefully add the kindling onto the tinder and work the fire up. If it doesn't respond a little blowing or fanning will give it more oxygen.

6 Having built the fire up, you can now bake your food in the oven below. Alternatively, and much more quickly, you can cook meat on an extra piece of tin held to one side of the fire.

Gathering fuel

Dead wood, as long as it's not actually lying in water, will usually have some dry material in it somewhere, but the best sources are dead timber that's still standing, and dead branches that are still attached to the tree. Look for the bark peeling off.

The main difference between kindling and fuel proper is its size. Remember, the kindling takes up the sparks and glowing embers from the tinder and turns it into flames that will ignite the fuel.

Small, bone-dry twigs are the best, but if necessary you can make 'firesticks' by shaving larger pieces with shallow cuts to feather them. Once again, this is a job much better done in advance.

Tinder must be dry. Absolutely, perfectly dry. You should have some

SOME NATURAL FIREMAKING MATERIALS

TINDER
Birch bark
Shredded inner bark from cedar, chestnut, red elm trees
Fine wood shavings
Dead grass, ferns, moss, fungi
Straw
Sawdust
Very fine pitch-wood scrapings
Dead evergreen needles
Rotted portions of dead logs or trees
Evergreen tree wood knots
Bird down (fine feathers)
Down seed heads
Fine, dried vegetable fibres
Spongy threads of dead puffball
Dead palm leaves

Skinlike membrane lining bamboo
Lint from pockets and seams
Charred cloth
Waxed paper
Outer bamboo shavings
Gunpowder
Cotton
Lint

KINDLING
Small twigs
Small strips of wood
Split wood
Heavy cardboard
Pieces of wood taken from inside larger pieces
Wood that has been soaked or doused in highly flammable

materials such as petrol, oil or wax
NB Must be completely dry!

FUEL
Dry standing wood and dry dead branches
Dry inside (heart) of fallen tree trunks and large branches
Green wood that is finely split
Dry grasses twisted into bunches
Peat dry enough to burn (may be found at the top of undercut banks)
Dried animal dung
Animal fats
Coal, oil shale or oil sand lying on the surface

Fire bows, saws and thongs

Fire Bow

Making a fire from the friction of wood upon wood really is a last-ditch alternative. The few aboriginal tribes that still make fire this way spend a very long time selecting exactly the right materials. Nevertheless, in the desert, where it's perfectly dry, it is possible to start a fire in this way.

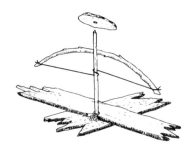

You'll need:
1 A piece of green hardwood, about a metre long and 2½ cm in diameter
2 A piece of dry hardwood, 30 cm long and 1 cm in diameter.
3 A 5-cm hardwood cube, or a shell or a suitable stone
4 A piece of dry softwood, 2½ cm thick
5 A cord for the bow-string.

To make the fire bow:
1 Make the bow loosely using the cord and the long piece of hardwood.
2 Round off one end of the short piece of hardwood, and taper the other slightly.
3 Carve out the centre of the hardwood cube to fit the taper, or find a stone or shell of the right shape.

4 Make a depression in the softwood, close to one edge, and make a groove from it that leads to the edge.
5 Put some tinder next to the end of the groove.
6 Loop the bow-string round the drill, maintain pressure on the top with the cap, and work the bow backwards and forwards to create friction between the hardwood drill and the softwood baseboard. Wood dust will build up in the groove, and the end of the drill will become red-hot and ignite it.

Fire Saw

You'll need:
1 A piece of bamboo, 5-8 cm in diameter and ½ metre long
2 A forked stick, to anchor it into the ground.

To make the fire saw:
1 Split the bamboo lengthways.
2 Cut two notches in a straight line across the two exposed edges near to one end.
3 Brace the notched bamboo with the forked stick.
4 Fill the space between the notches with a handful of tinder.
5 Saw in the notches until the tinder ignites.

Fire Thongs

1 Make a thong (a strip or string of tough material) using rattan (a sort of tropical vine), leather or very tough cord.
2 Split a dry stick and hold the split open with a small wedge.
3 Run the thong through the split.
4 Place a small wad of tinder in the split.
5 Secure the stick with your foot and run the thong back and forth to create frictional heat. The tinder will eventually ignite.

already, packed up securely in a water-tight box next to your skin. If not, you'll have to find some.

Don't look too far to start with: you won't need very much. Try the lining of your pockets and the seams of your clothes. The lint that collects there makes good tinder, except for wool. Dry bark, shredded into tiny pieces; dead grass, fern and moss; dead pine needles; downy seedheads from thistles and similar plants: all these make good tinder, as long as the material is dry.

The common factor is the size of the individual pieces or fibres. They must be tiny, so that as much of their substance as possible is exposed to the air and to the spark or flame.

The vital spark

If you don't have matches or a lighter that works, there are several alternative ways to start a fire.

If you have direct sunlight and a magnifying lens, you can use the glass to focus the sun's rays onto the tinder and start it burning that way. But this won't work at night in a rainstorm!

Flint and steel

Alternatively, you could use the 'flint and steel' method.

If you have a so-called 'metal match' (a metal strip with tiny flint chips embedded in it), then use that, scraping your knife blade along it to produce a shower of sparks.

Or look for a piece of flint or other

very hard stone. Then you can use your knife to strike sparks off it; use the back of the blade. If you have a piece of hacksaw blade, you should use that to save damaging your knife.

Alternative technology

There are two other ways of making fire. The bow and drill and the fire saw both rely on friction between two pieces of wood. You have to make a small part of one of those pieces hot enough to set the tinder going. It is possible – but you'll only need to try it once to become fanatical about carrying matches with you everywhere you go!

If you have a vehicle you have another option – use the battery. Rip

If you've got this kit with you, you can light a fire under any conditions. You don't need all of it; a stove would make your life easier, but if you can't carry one you can make your own oven.

out some wire and attach a piece to each terminal. Touch the bare ends together and you'll get a spark.

If the vehicle is petrol driven, you can use a tiny amount of the fuel to help the process along, but remember that petrol in its liquid form doesn't burn. You can only set fire to it as a vapour. So, use less than a teaspoonful, soak some rag and make the spark into the air just above the surface. Diesel fuel doesn't work in this way — you need a good size flame to set it alight at all.

1 Matches
Service issue matches, found in survival packs, are books of paper matches weatherproofed by vacuum sealing in aluminium foil. The foil can also be used with tinder as fuel.

2 Folding stove
The service issue stove comes with a box of hexamine tablets, which can be used as fuel or broken up and used with tinder in firelighting.

3 Jelled alcohol stove
This is used mostly in the Arctic and by covert surveillance units and patrols in Northern Ireland, because of the absence of smoke and smells. The fuel can be topped up with inflammable jellies such as contact adhesive. The fire is put out by replacing the cap and therefore breaking the fire triangle by removing oxygen from the heat and fuel.

4 Zippo lighter
The Zippo is perhaps the best all-purpose lighter available, supposed to light first time in all weathers if it has fuel. When fuel runs out, other inflammable liquids can be used. Spare flints should be kept under the wadding of the lighter's fuel tank.

5 Tallow candle
Don't try to light your fire with a match; you could waste them all. Instead, light the candle in a sheltered spot and light your fire from it. Tallow is animal fat and in an emergency could provide food. In the absence of tallow, you could use joke birthday candles as these will usually relight if blown out by the wind.

6 Lifeboat matches
These are special long-burning waterproofed matches in a waterproof container. Contrary to accepted practice, it is not a good idea to split your matches into quarters or more as this can reduce their efficiency.

7 Potassium permanganate crystals
A useful addition to your survival kit as it can be used as an antiseptic, a gargle for throat infections, snow marker etc. For firelighting it should be combined with glycerine and sugar,

and will then spontaneously combust. Sugar will be found in your compo pack; glycerine is a constituent of antifreeze, and you could try using some from a vehicle.

8 Magnesium block
Scrape some slivers of magnesium off the block onto your tinder with your knife. Then use a section of hacksaw blade from your escape kit to ignite it by striking it off the flint on top of the magnesium block.

9 Ammunition
The powder contents of the cartridge can be used to help fire your tinder. You can also wedge a cloth in the cartridge once the ball or projectiles have been removed and chamber the round into your weapon. Aim at the tinder and fire. The cloth will be shot out smouldering.

10 Calcium carbide lighter
When water is added to calcium carbide it produces acetylene gas, which can be ignited with a spark.

11 Aluminium shavings
These can be mixed with tinder to help ignite and maintain the fire.

12 Flint and steel
A flint rod will produce sparks when steel (a piece of hacksaw blade) is drawn across it. The two should be kept together with a piece of nylon cord.

13 Chemical heaters
The contents of these can be mixed carefully with tinder to produce a fire. Other chemicals such as potassium chlorate and sugar can be ignited by sugar or using sulphuric acid from a car battery. Potassium chlorate is found in some weedkillers and also some throat lozenges.

14 Cotton wool
You can use the cotton wool absorbent layers of your combat dressing as tinder: open the dressing and cut through the lint at the back, allowing the dressing to remain sterile on its wound face so that it can still be used. Other tinder can be salvaged from pocket linings, old rope, fine wood shavings, dry bark, grasses or ferns, pine needles etc.

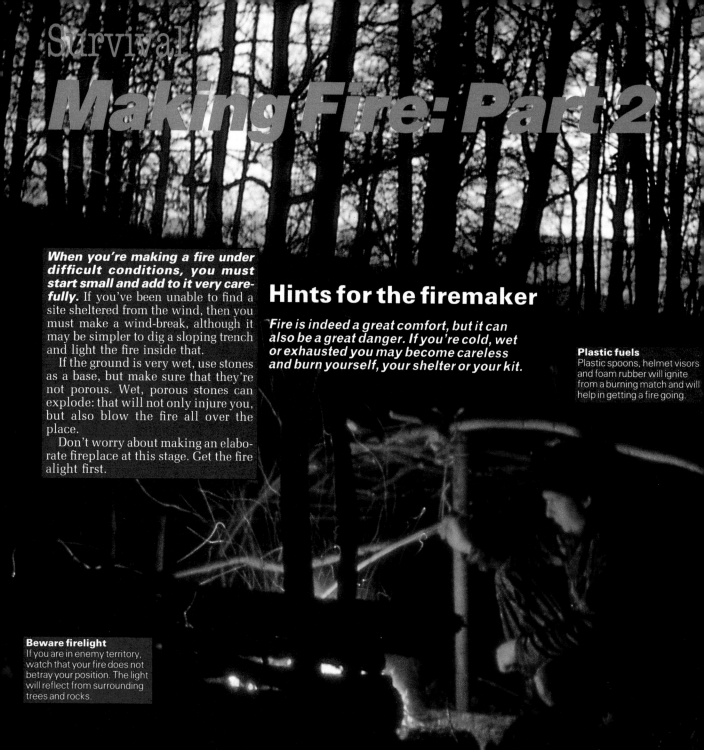

When you're making a fire under difficult conditions, you must start small and add to it very carefully. If you've been unable to find a site sheltered from the wind, then you must make a wind-break, although it may be simpler to dig a sloping trench and light the fire inside that.

If the ground is very wet, use stones as a base, but make sure that they're not porous. Wet, porous stones can explode: that will not only injure you, but also blow the fire all over the place.

Don't worry about making an elaborate fireplace at this stage. Get the fire alight first.

Hints for the firemaker

Fire is indeed a great comfort, but it can also be a great danger. If you're cold, wet or exhausted you may become careless and burn yourself, your shelter or your kit.

Plastic fuels
Plastic spoons, helmet visors and foam rubber will ignite from a burning match and will help in getting a fire going.

Beware firelight
If you are in enemy territory, watch that your fire does not betray your position. The light will reflect from surrounding trees and rocks.

Smoke signals
Smoke tends to go straight up in cold, calm weather, making a beacon to your position. In warmer weather smoke tends to hug the ground, making it less visible but betraying your position by its smell.

Careful cutting
Cut low tree branches for firewood rather than an entire tree. Fallen trees are easily spotted by enemy aircraft.

Smoke differences
The wood from coniferous trees (pine, larch, spruce etc) will give off more smoke than wood from deciduous (broadleaf) trees.

Other fuels
Dried moss, bundled grass or peat (old, dried-out reed beds) will make a productive slow-burning fuel.

Selecting and preparing the site

Think about the right place to build your fire:

1 Why do you need a fire – is it for warmth, to cook on or to dry off wet clothing? Do you need it close to your shelter?
2 Are you in hostile terrain? Do you have to be secretive?
3 How long are you going to be at your site? If it's for a long time, it's worth building a proper structure.
4 Select a site away from wind and in a position to reflect the heat in the direction you need it.
5 Build your fire near a good source of firemaking materials.

Laying a fire

The basic structure of a new fire is vital. Remember, the fire will need lots of air, so arrange your kindling in a cone around the tinder. Alternatively, leave the kindling against a larger log.

Make a nest of dry grass and the smallest twigs. If you can find a dry bird's or mouse's nest, so much the better. It will have down and fur mixed in with the grass, and probably some dry droppings too – all of them excellent tinder.

Put your tinder inside. Arrange dry kindling over it in the shape of a cone, or make a lean-to by pushing a green stick into the ground at an angle of about thirty degrees and build up the kindling along it to make a sort of tent.

Make sure that you've got all the materials you'll need to hand before attempting to light the fire – you may only get one chance, and at the beginning you'll have to work quickly, adding small amounts of kindling as the fire grows.

Keep the fire going

If you have a choice of different types of wood to use as fuel, use softwood – pine and spruce, for example – as the first load of fuel, but be careful of sparks. These woods contain resin and burn quickly. To keep the fire

Reflectors and windbreaks

Construct a simple log wall on the side of the fire away from you and your shelter. This will reflect the heat, and provide a windbreak. And as a bonus it will dry out the next batch of logs for use.

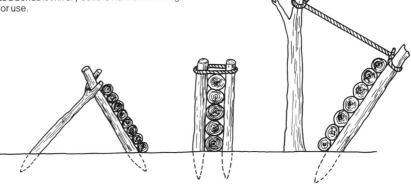

These survivors have built themselves a cosy set-up, with shelter, log fire and reflector all at close quarters. But you should watch the problems of smoke and the possibility of the shelter itself catching fire.

The log cabin pile

This is a very good way of laying a fire. Plenty of air can circulate and it will not collapse until it's well away.

going, use hardwood such as oak or beech. They're much longer lasting.

You can use a mixture of green and dry wood to keep the fire going through the night, but don't just dump wood on it without thinking. Make sure that you keep a good stock of fuel close at hand, and arrange it so that the heat from the fire will help to dry the fuel out. Keep kindling at hand too, so that you can revive the fire quickly if it looks like dying out.

Improving the fire

How you improve the fire site depends on what you're going to use it for.

A fire that you use for smoking food, for instance, isn't much use for anything else. Its purpose is to produce

Cooking food

A small, slow-burning fire is the best for cooking. Raging naked flames will produce burned hands and scorched, inedible food.

The hobo stove

A simple stove made from an old tin or oildrum conserves heat and produces a stable, useful 'hotplate'.

A simple crane

Use a green wood pole with a forked notch to hold a container over a fire. Beware large naked flames: a burning pole will wreck your meal.

Underground fireplace

This is an old Red Indian arrangement. Make one or more vents on the upwind side of the fire for ventilation. It will reduce smoke and flame and the effects of high winds.

lots of smoke inside an enclosure. You won't be able to cook on it, and it won't give out much warmth.

You can cook on an open fire, but it's not too efficient: it's better to construct a stove of some sort. The simplest stove needs something like a five-gallon oil drum. Punch holes in one end and in a ring all around the side at the same end. Cut out a panel about two inches above that ring of holes. Punch a large hole in one side of the drum near the other end, to let the smoke out. Place the stove on a ring of stones to allow the air to circulate from underneath.

Now you can transfer some of your fire into the stove, stoke it through the cut-out panel and cook on top. It'll give off enough heat to keep you warm, too, and has the very positive benefit of not showing sparks and flames like an open fire does.

A rabbit becomes dinner on a spit. This fancy arrangement works OK as long as the fire isn't too strong and you're able to keep revolving the spit with the meal attached. You must cook wild food really thoroughly; a quick scorch on the outside and blood on the inside is a recipe for food poisoning or worse.

The fire pit

You can achieve much the same effect by digging a circular pit, and then another smaller one, slantwise, that meets it at the bottom. The slanting hole is for the air to circulate up through the fire, so dig it on the side of the prevailing wind.

If you dig it close to the trunk of a tree, the smoke will go up into the foliage and be dispersed, helping to disguise your position.

Making a Maori oven

This is a simple, efficient oven that can be made as big as you need, even to cook a whole deer. Once set up you can leave it to look after itself while you get on with other important things.

1 Dig a hole about 60 × 60 × 60 cm. Put very hot (red hot if possible) stones in the bottom. Cover with moss, ferns or other foliage. Make a second, smaller layer.

2 Wrap the portioned meat in foliage, making sure you don't use toxic plants, and place in the pit on top of the stones.

3 Place more foliage on top of the meat. Place an upright stick in the centre of the stove area and pile the excavated earth on top of the pit.

4 Withdraw the stick and pour about 2 pints of water into the pit. Steam will pour out, so cover with a large stone. After about two hours the meat will have been pressure-cooked and will fall from the bone.

You can make a fire more effective as a source of warmth by building a firewall across one or two sides, to reflect the heat back towards you.

Two in one

The simplest way is to drive four green-wood stakes into the ground in two pairs three or four inches apart, with three or four feet between them. Fill up the space with trimmed branches and trunks, but don't bind them together. That way you get a firewall and a stack of dry wood all in one!

You may have to build your fire in the wet – on snow, or in a swamp, for example. In the snow it's easiest to build a base out of layers of green wood. In swamp or marsh land, raise that platform up on four legs.

Don't bother to chop or even break up long pieces of wood for an open fire. Start at one end and feed the log in as it burns, or lay it across the fire and wait until it burns through, then turn the ends in.

Having gone through all the pain of getting your fire going, don't let it go out! Use well-dried hardwood during the day; it produces very little smoke. As the evening approaches, you may want to add green or damp fuel to produce smoke that will drive away insects.

Alternative fuels

If you have a vehicle, almost every part of it that isn't metal will burn.

Mix oil, petrol or diesel with sand in a pit and set fire to it. Rip out the upholstery and the trim and use for fuel.

The tyres will burn if you get them hot enough, but stay upwind of the smoke! Hydraulic fluid from the brake and clutch systems is highly flammable, and so is neat anti-freeze. All of this applies to aircraft as much as ground vehicles.

Animal droppings, if they are perfectly dry, are a very good source of fuel: easy to light, slow-burning and almost smokeless.

After a while, looking after your fire will become second nature to you. You'll sense changes in its moods, and be able to change its character to do different jobs.

Fighting Fit

AT THE AIRHEAD

When most people hear the word 'Airborne', they automatically think of the Parachute Regiment, whose men form the infantry arm of 5 Airborne Brigade. However, the Paras would cease to function were it not for other, equally important, units. Besides its four infantry battalions, 5 Airborne consists of armoured recce, artillery and engineer regiments and a signal squadron. Medical support is provided by a Para Field Ambulance unit, and logistic support from the recently formed Logistic Battalion.

Dual role

The role of 5 Airborne Brigade is twofold. Its primary requirement is that of home defence, but of equal importance is its commitment to out-of-area operations. During a large-scale operation, the brigade would combine with 3 Commando Brigade, falling under the command of a Joint Force Headquarters.

After passing P Company, those wishing to serve in the parachute role in the Brigade undergo the four-week parachute training course at RAF Brize Norton.

As part of 5 Airborne Brigade you can expect to operate in your own specialist role, adapting it to the requirements of airborne operations. Regular exercises help everyone practise unit co-operation.

Salisbury Plain

For example, you may find yourself on a logistics exercise on Salisbury Plain. Although primarily a service and supply exercise, with the Logistic battalion sorting out the enormous problems of keeping the brigade functioning, each unit would be allocated its own tasks. The infantrymen, of course, must push on to take their objectives, supported when necessary by the gunners. Casualties, quickly flown back to the airhead, would be tended by 23 Para Field Ambulance. In the midst of all the apparent chaos and confusion of battle would be the Royal Engineers 9 Para Squadron!

In 9 Para Squadron your role is to provide Engineers support for the brigade. The squadron consists of three

Below: The Army's latest all-purpose vehicle is the six-wheel-drive all-terrain Supacat. It is ideal for airborne use, although not quite as useful in a scrap as the BMD or the mighty SO 120 operated by the Warsaw Pact.

Above: Good command and control of Engineer assets is essential due to the very wide range of tasks they have to complete, with a huge variety of stores throughout the operational area. Para Engineers have two command vehicles to deal with this mammoth task.

Above: Engineer work is always varied, and the difference between infantry skills and engineer skills is that on the exercise you can actually do what you would do in war, e.g. laying mats for the Harrier pad or laying mines.

Above: An engineer carefully removes enemy shaped cutting charges from the damaged bridge. Like all engineers, he is are fully trained in the engineer use of explosives.

Left: Para Engineers are expected to fight as infantry where required. In this case, 9 Squadron was involved in the assault on an enemy reserve demolition at crossing point Charlie and managed to capture it before the demolition was completely blown.

field troops (50 men each), support troop, and a troop from 33 Engineer Regiment (EOD). Squadron strength is presently about 200, although with men away on courses etc you normally deploy on exercise with around 150 personnel. On ops, of course, everyone would be available.

Once the logistic exercise is under way, the squadron finds itself spread throughout the exercise area. The support troop establishes an HQ at the airhead, a secure base where stores and resupplies arrive. Prisoners of war, casualties and evacuees all end up at the airhead prior to being flown out. It is a hotbed of activity, with vehicles, Hercules aircraft and helicopters of all types continually arriving and departing.

Water supply

The three field troops are each engaged in very different tasks. In order to keep the brigade supplied with fresh water, one of your first priorities is to construct a filtration system and chlorinator to purify water pumped from a nearby natural source. The water is then stored on top of a Cup-Lock tower in a 1100-litre tank. With the water purification unit installed, One Troop is then detailed to construct a Harrier strip – including a taxiway, operating pad and a big hide for the aircraft.

Laying the taxiway

Starting from scratch means you have to level the area, using sandbags where necessary, before laying the taxiway of steel Harrier matting. The taxiway runs in a circle to a square landing pad and back into an aircraft pen, with steel poles supporting overhead camouflage netting. Two Troop is temporarily engaged in playing enemy, while Three Troop is scheduled to parachute in to the exercise along with 3 Para during the afternoon of Day Four.

Hundreds of parachutes

The drop goes in at 15.30 hrs. Wave upon wave of C-130s roar over Salisbury Plain, leaving the sky filled with parachutes. Hundreds of men are dropped, along with Land Rovers and trailers secured to medium stressed platforms (MSPs). Twenty minutes after the drop, it begins to pour with rain. Typical Salisbury Plain weather!

A Chinook choppers in a load of Bar Mines for use in the Engineer Bar Mine Layer. A trained team can lay 400 to 600 mines in an hour with a towing vehicle – far faster than planting Mk 7s by hand.

Transport brings up a pallet of Medium Girder Bridge from the airhead. The bridge is made up of aluminium alloy sections that are fitted together by hand.

The first vehicle moves across the bridge just one and a half hours after the arrival of the bridge kit. The kit requires a six-man lift for two major components, but everything else is a four-man job.

Fighting Fit

That evening sees 3 Para having completed their main task, involving the rescue of hundreds of civilian 'hostages' – actually the families of the paras themselves. The women and children are choppered back to the airhead in an operation lasting many hours.

Meanwhile, One Troop has completed the Harrier strip, and everyone is just preparing to settle down for the night when a sentry notices approaching soldiers. You are stood-to, and minutes later find yourself fighting off a half-hearted attack mounted by elements of 7 RHA, 3 Para and the French 1^e Regiment de Chasseurs Parachutistes! As the assault peters out, someone quietly points out that the objective is actually another wood on a hill several hundred metres distant!

The next day sees elements of 9 Squadron accompanying an attack against Crossing Point Charlie – one of several bridges in the area. The bridge is taken, but not in time to stop the defenders from partially destroying the structure. The engineers are required to move in a medium girder bridge – capable of carrying up to Class 70 (80 tons) of weight. It takes just 1½ hours to complete the bridge and for the first vehicle to roll across.

Minefield belt

In the late afternoon, all three troops are detailed to lay a minefield obstacle belt. A Chinook airlifts Three Troop to its location. The helicopter also carries a Supacat – the first time that the nifty little vehicle has been transported in this way.

On Monday morning there is another heavy drop when an air-portable bridge is parachuted in. The APB, a lightweight bridge capable of carrying about 9 tons, is considered to be the squadron speciality. You begin to erect it that evening, working under cover of darkness to complete the job – the squadron's last major task of the exercise.

It is all good practice in case 9 Squadron ever has to support the brigade in a real combat situation. In limited war, a battalion may well assault with 9 Para Squadron combat engineers actually leading the way through minefields and other obstacles – a daunting task but, like any other, one that the Para Engineers are more than capable of carrying out.

A 9 Sqn engineer prepares to convert an anti-tank minefield into a mixed minefield at the flick of a switch, using the Ranger anti-personnel mining system.

The heavy drops come in smack on the DZ markers, care of Para RCT air despatchers from Hercules aircraft. The drop includes an air-portable bridge.

The engineers set to work preparing the bridge pallet for the move to the crossing point. This lightweight bridge is capable of carrying all the brigade's vehicles, but not armour of any weight.

Combat Report
South Africa:
Pathfinder Raid on Angola

A former sergeant and communications specialist in The Pathfinder Company, South African Parachute Brigade, describes a successful raid.

In August 1981 South Africa launched a highly successful raid against enemy forces in southern Angola. Code-named 'Operation Protea', the attack was designed to neutralise SWAPO (South West African People's Organisation) forces in the area while demoralising the Angolans to such a degree that they would be forced to seriously reconsider their support of the guerrilla movement.

The invasion force was assembled in total secrecy. Infantry, artillery and armoured units were flown to Grootfontein in South West Africa (Namibia), under the illusion that they were merely part of a routine field exercise. But after being formed into battle groups and task forces, each unit found itself undergoing two weeks of intensive manoeuvres. Clearly we were being prepared for something special.

Pathfinder Company was created by Colonel Jan Brëytenbach. who commanded 44 Parachute Brigade. He was the originator of the elite Recce Commandos and the infamous '32' Battalion. Unlike most units of the South African Defence Force, we Pathfinders were almost exclusively white mercenaries; many were seasoned veterans of the Rhodesian war. In fact, the only South African in the group was our commander, Captain Botha!

The attack goes in

We travelled in nine specially-equipped vehicles: three Toyota Land Cruisers and three Land Rovers, the latter having been stripped down and rebuilt along the lines of the armed Land Rovers used by the British SAS. To carry fuel, ammunition and other supplies we used armed 2.5 Mercedes Unimog trucks. Our strength varied between 30 and 40 men, and we had spent many months fighting in northern Namibia and southern Angola, often in conjunction with 32 Battalion.

We left our base at Ondangwa at 0800 hours on 19 August, and on arrival at Omuthiya we were attached to Combat Group 40 in Task Force 'Alpha'. We received our final briefing on the morning of the 22nd: our Task Force was to attack the Angolan armoured brigade in the town of Xangongo, codenamed 'Target Yankee'. We were assigned as tank hunters, to be kept in reserve and deployed as required.

The attack went in at 0230 on Monday 24 August, but the Pathfinders did not have a very exciting time until late on Tuesday night. We

Among the Angolan vehicles we captured were Russian T-34s from World War II.

had laagered 200 metres off the main Xangongo-Cahama road while a company of Ratels (wheeled armoured cars) were deployed across the road about 1 km to the north. At about 2200 hrs I was wakened by one of the others, an excited Dave Beam.

"There's a convoy of trucks driving up the road", he said.

"Yeah," I replied, "so what?"

"They're petrol-driven"

"Yeah, so?"

"Well, ours are all diesel!"

Obviously an Angolan force had got between us and the Ratels. There was instant pandemonium as we were hurriedly alerted and stood to, and meanwhile we heard a savage firefight erupt between the South Africans to the south and the Angolans. The contact went on for five or 10 minutes and was followed by an ominous silence, broken by the sound of approaching vehicles.

We settled ourselves behind our guns as the FAPLA (Popular Front for the Liberation of Angola) convoy rolled closer and closer. Then, as the trucks drew level with our position, the column drew to a halt! Amazingly, the Angolans had decided to reorganise immediately within our killing zone.

The fighting raged

On a command from Colonel Brëytenbach, the vehicles nearest the enemy opened up with their .50 cals, MAGs and a 14.5; the crews from the vehicles facing away from the enemy assisted them by firing M79s and a 60-mm mortar. FAPLA replied with small arms and a number of 23-mm twin-barrelled anti-aircraft guns. Red and green tracer tore into the bush and arced away into the pitch-black night, while an artillery battery a few klicks south added to the surrealist effect by sending over illumination shells that bathed the scene in an eerie, artificial yellow light.

The fighting raged for about 15 minutes before the enemy ceased firing. Somehow we had escaped any damage to ourselves or our vehicles. Noises from the far side of the road indicated that at least some of FAPLA were also still alive and kicking, and possibly even setting up mortars!

Both vehicles exploded

A patrol armed with 89-mm rocket-launchers was hurriedly formed under our OC, Captain Botha, and led towards the ominous sounds. After venturing a short distance into the bush on the opposite side of the road our men spotted several soldiers busily setting up mortars beside two Russian-built GAZ trucks. Captain Botha quickly lined up the patrol which, on his order, opened fire.

It was dramatically effective. Both vehicles exploded after direct hits from the 89-mm rockets, whereupon FAPLA disappeared in disarray. After only a few minutes of intensive shooting Captain Botha ordered his men to cease firing. There was now neither sight nor sound of the enemy. However, due to the dangers inherent in sweeping a contact area in the dark, the patrol decided to return to the laager.

At first light we stood to while one man from each crew brewed up some tea (without which we could barely function)! Thus revitalised, we mounted up and pulled out on to the road, where we saw the extent of our night's work.

The entire FAPLA convoy had been abandoned. Attesting to the success of the ambush were 14 vehicles: two BTR armoured

All our vehicles were specially equipped, and the Rovers were rebuilt in the same way as the ones used by the British SAS.

cars, two BM 21 Stalin-Organs (truck mounted rocket-launchers), seven GAZ trucks (four of them mounting 23-mm AA guns), a fully-laden radio jeep, and the two destroyed mortar trucks! Although no bodies were found, it was evident from the quantity of blood spoor that casualties had been removed under the cover of darkness.

Salvaging the kit

We now set about helping ourselves to FAPLA abandoned personal kit, each man collecting a Russian helmet and Cuban-made FAPLA camouflage uniform. After being loaded with spare equipment the captured jeep was retained for our own use, and the other vehicles were left for our troops to salvage later on. Upon completing our search of the area our convoy headed south, back to Xangongo.

'Operation Protea' was my last action with the Pathfinders. On 28 August, during an attack on the village of Chilau, my Toyota ran over a landmine. Colonel Brëytenbach and our driver Lance Penner were unhurt, but Dave Beam lost both legs and I received serious injuries to my left foot.

After three months in hospital I decided to bid farewell to southern Africa. Shortly afterwards, the Pathfinders became political casualties, and in early 1982 the unit was disbanded.

The Pathfinders were nearly all white mercenaries, many of them veterans from the Rhodesian war. The only South African was the commander. Kit used in the field was pretty informal.

THE PATHFINDERS

Pathfinder Platoon consists of some 32 individuals whose primary role is to recce and mark Drop Zones (DZs) prior to the main airborne assault. As a Pathfinder you may well be expected to mount surveillance operations both before and after the drop. You are likely to find yourself involved in medium- or long-range reconnaissance patrols, and will probably be required to carry out close target recces (CTRs), ambushes and raids.

Eligibility and testing

The platoon is open to all para-trained members of 5 Airborne Brigade who have the character and determination to pass the gruelling three-week selection cadre. At present, this is conducted at Aldershot and in the hills around Brecon, in mid-Wales. For those who pass selection, there is the opportunity to specialise in a number of skills, of which one of the more exciting must be military free-fall parachuting.

So as to be able to arrive at a location quickly yet silently, all Pathfinders must become proficient in High Altitude Low Opening (HALO) parachuting techniques. This is quite different to normal operations, where you leap out of an aircraft at 800 ft and rely on a static line to deploy your parachute for you! HALO means exiting at heights between 12,000 and 25,000 ft and being prepared to deploy the parachute yourself. It may sound straightforward, but there is a lot to learn.

High altitude hazards

Consider the lack of oxygen at altitude. The Royal Air Force has C-130s specially equipped with oxygen units, enabling troops to ascend to altitudes beyond 10,000 ft – the 'official' maximum recommended air breathable height. Any higher, and you must use a Pressure Demand Oxygen Regulator. When set to air-mix, this ensures that increasing amounts of oxygen are supplied automatically, so that by the time you reach 30,000 ft, you are breathing pure oxygen.

The effects of oxygen deficiency, or

Equipment has to be carefully checked before and after fitting. The parachute is totally different from static line chutes: the canopy is deployed by the parachutist and is steerable to allow the individual to run into the target. Both the reserve and the main chute are carried on the back.

hypoxia, are similar to being drunk, but the consequences are far more serious. To teach you to recognise the symptoms you have to experience hypoxia during controlled tests in a decompression chamber, where you will be told to remove your oxygen mask and perform tasks such as writing the alphabet backwards. With hypoxia, such a simple exercise becomes unbelievably difficult!

Practical parachuting

Besides learning about the physiology of respiration at high altitude, there is the practical side of parachuting to consider. How do you maintain the free-fall 'X' position? How can you increase the rate of descent, or 'track' *across* the sky? What happens if you should lose stability – how would you regain control?

Free-fall looks so easy when you see it on television. The parachutist appears to be suspended in mid-air. Until you actually try it for yourself, it seems impossible that he is rocketing earthwards at a terrifying 120 mph!

After qualifying, you practise HALO techniques during regular sessions such as the twice-yearly Exercise Quick Drop. You have to commute for a week between Aldershot and an RAF base, and in order to get in the required number of descents this usually means having to make an early start!

Boarding the aircraft

You muster at 06.55 hours for the journey to Royal Air Force Lyneham. A four-tonner takes you straight onto the airfield, where you debus alongside a waiting C-130 Hercules aircraft. Parachutes, and Bergens, helmets, oxygen masks and altimeters are all laid out, and everyone carefully checks each item of equipment before kitting up.

Before boarding you will want to know the latest Met. reports. Is low cloud likely to cause problems with visibility? What is the present wind speed? These and other details relevant to the drop are provided in a briefing by the RAF. At last, it's time to walk up the tail ramp into the Hercules.

In the air

Once airborne, you unfasten your seat belt, stand up and secure your Bergen beneath your parachute pack, where it now becomes an uncomfortable seat. Next, you fit helmets and oxygen mask, and then wait. And wait. You run over the drills in your mind, mentally preparing yourself for

Descents are made from RAF Hercules at a height where the engine noise cannot be heard by anyone on the ground. Here the pilot is being given the instruction to start number four engine.

The interior of the Hercules is not a pleasant environment, but at least it is not as crowded as on a normal static line drop. Once the aircraft is airborne you are free to move around and fit the Para Bergen.

The Bergen is fitted upside down so that it rests behind the back of your legs. This arrangement makes it possible to manoeuvre in the air. Note the white cord, which attaches the Bergen in quick-release to the parachutist.

Above: Oxygen masks are required for heights of over 10,000ft. The idea of jumping at this height is that the enemy will not know you are dropping in, and DZs will be chosen well away from enemy positions.

Below: The team waits for the red light for standby. They will aim to exit the aircraft together and stay close throughout the descent so that they land together.

Fighting Fit

the jump ahead.

At 25,000 ft you are brought back to the present when the tail ramp begins to slowly open. After the dim aircraft lighting, the brightness outside dazzles you.

Time to jump

But there's little time to admire the view. Yours is the first section to jump. Again you stagger to your feet. Here we go, then. Red light on! You shuffle aft and quickly fit your goggles. Green on! You rush towards the gaping doorway and leap headlong into space. Falling, you cartwheel once, catching a glimpse of the Hercules as it appears to accelerate away from you at a crazy angle. A patch of blue sky and then the cotton wool-like clouds far below as you regain control and stabilise your position, arms and legs outstretched and your body offering maximum resistance to the earth's gravitational pull.

The way down

You'll drop for around one minute 50 seconds, during which time you must try to keep station with the other three patrol members. You plummet through the cloud. Check height... Ten thousand feet... Six thousand... Everyone now separates slightly so as not to get in each other's way when the automatic opening device opens your parachute pack.

The canopy deploys, jerking you upright and immediately slowing your rate of descent. Relief! OK, all-round observation and then formate on the lowest man in your patrol so that you can all land together. At 1,000 ft you make sure that your canopy is airing into wind, then un-hook your Bergen, leaving it dangling at the end of its nylon line.

Made it!

The ground seems to rush up to meet you. You pull down on both steering toggles simultaneously, causing the ram-air parachute to stall, which allows a gentle landing.

Standing up, you unfasten your oxygen mask and remove helmet and goggles. Everyone else looks all right. A good jump!

If this were a real operation you would of course hide your parachute prior to continuing with the mission. On exercise, you have to roll up your own 'chute and make your way to the pick-up point to wait for the transport back to Lyneham – where the aircraft will be waiting for the day's second lift!

Green on, and the team disappears off the back ramp of the Hercules. Note the tight formation and the stand, ready to somersault into a stable spread position. The kit layout provides the most stable flight profile.

The drop is just a means to an end, to get the Pathfinder on the ground to do his job: this could be anything from a raid to recce patrols. Recce is perhaps the most important of the unit's tasks.

Training for the job is extremely rigorous. Pathfinders are required to operate without support for long periods, which requires very high standards of mental and physical fitness and individual initiative.

Combat Report
Aden:
Arab Mutineer Attack

Iain Reid, a paratrooper, tells how he and his section came under fire from mutinous Arab soldiers in Aden in June 1967.

After completing my parachute training in November 1966 at the age of 17½, I was posted to 8 Platoon, 'C' Company. In March the following year we were sent to Aden.

The battalion was stationed at Radfan Camp, about three miles from the town of Sheik Othman, a hotbed of terrorism. Located about 1½ miles from our camp was the Federal National Guard (FNG) Barracks, known as 'Champion Lines'.

The FNG were Arabs, comprising the armed paramilitary force of the police. There had been several armed clashes between the FNG and the Federal Regular Army. Terrorist organisations, the NLF (National Liberation Front) and FLOSY (Front Liberation of Southern Yemen), had members within both of these units.

In April and May various acts of terrorism were carried out by these two factions, resulting in a number of deaths among the British forces and the civilian population.

The FNG mutiny

In June my company was on standby within Radfan Camp. Earlier that day our commanding officer had been informed by Brigade HQ that a mutiny by the FNG was taking place at Champion Lines. At about 10 a.m. my section was tasked to move, and 2nd Lieutenant Emson, our platoon commander, was briefed.

Numerous Arab soldiers had opened fire on passing British military vehicles, and casualties

Guard duty at Radfan camp. Nearby lay the 'Champion Lines', home of the Federal National Guard, which mutinied and attacked the British troops who were supposed to be training them.

were later confirmed as eight dead. Lieutenant Emson briefed us, and after checking our equipment we all loaded on to an 'Armoured Pig'.

This vehicle consisted of a steel body mounted on a Bedford chassis, and was effective against small-arms and machine-gun fire. All along the sides were gun slits. At the front, the driver and observer had two slits which could be opened if required.

Our mission was to proceed to the barracks and rescue or assist any wounded personnel we might find.

All quiet . . .

Apart from Lieutenant Emson, the section consisted of Corporal Dave Holbert, regimental signaller; Lance-Corporal Bob Musgrave (ex Foreign Legion), section commander; and privates Mick Patey, Taff Francis, Lingard Richards and Ginge Wharton and me, all riflemen. The driver of the 'Pig' was Billy Hunter, on attachment from 63 Para Sqn, Royal Corps of Transport. Apart from Dave Holbert and Bob Musgrave, who had seen previous active service, we were all inexperienced.

Lieutenant Emson told Billy Hunter to drive slowly on the approach road to the barracks, to show the FNG that we were not an attacking force.

When we arrived we saw several army Land Rovers that had been badly shot up. There was also a Rover, belonging to the Arab Civil Police. A quick glimpse confirmed that there were several bodies lying beside these vehicles. Lieutenant Emson instructed Hunter to position our vehicle facing the barracks.

At this time we thought everything had quietened down and that loyal Arab officers had disarmed the mutineers. No-one had fired at us, and because of this both the front hatches of the 'Pig' were open, to give the front-seaters a better view. I was seated at the rear of the vehicle; opposite me was Bob Musgrave. Lieutenant Emson told us to open the rear doors, and as soon as we did so a young Arab civilian policeman came running towards us, clutching a gunshsot wound in his right side. Bob Musgrave and I pulled him in to the 'Pig'.

Rounds came in

Immediately an Arab in civilian dress appeared, screaming that he was a policeman and begging for help. At that instant, we came under heavy rifle and machine-gun fire from the barracks. Several rounds landed near the policeman and, tragically, he panicked and ran back towards his own vehicle and was shot dead.

Lieutenant Emson and Billy Hunter began to close the front hatches, but the driver's one refused to budge. Several rifles opened fire, and two of our tyres were burst.

Rounds started to come into the vehicle through the open hatch. The first person to be hit was Dave Holbert; both of his legs were smashed. Then Billy Hunter was hit in the chest. Still Lieutenant Emson could not close the hatch.

I don't remember being frightened; I was on an incredible high because of the adrenalin that was flowing. My mates seemed to be in the same state, as there was no panic or confusion. It was probably due to our training, and in any case we were occupied with trying to help the wounded as best we could.

More rounds came into the vehicle, and Lingard was hit in the neck. He fell to the floor in front of me and Bob Musgrave, and said quite

Ferret armoured cars probe the crater area of Aden, hotbed of Arab-organized terrorism. The paramilitary National Guard also traded shots with the regular Army units.

quietly, "I've been hit".

Miraculously, the bullet had missed his jugular vein by a fraction. Blood was pouring out of the wound. We placed his dressing over it, and within seconds it was saturated in blood. I added my own dressing, which managed to stem the flow. Lingard, quiet as a lamb, held the dressings tightly against his neck and sat upright on the floor.

Due to pain and lapses into unconsciousness, Dave Holbert was unable to use the radio, so Lieutenant Emson transmitted, asking for urgent assistance, and sent a casualty report.

In the firing line

It could only be a matter of time before I got hit. Incoming rounds were still entering through the hatch, ricocheting around the interior. Would it hurt? Were my mates thinking the same? Lingard was still sitting on the floor. I kept asking him if he was all right; I was worried that if he passed out he would die.

Lieutenant Emson decided to try to drive the 'Pig' broadside on to give some sort of protection. The only problem was that he couldn't drive, so Billy Hunter, although wounded and in pain, would have to tell him what to do. As Emson climbed into the driver's seat more rounds came in, and the ricochets hit Bob Musgrave in the back. His shirt was immediately covered in blood but it turned out to be only shrapnel.

Now directly in the firing line, Lieutenant Emson managed to turn the 'Pig' broadside on. This brave act prevented any further casualties inside the vehicle but the firing continued, and all our tyres were burst by this time.

Suddenly the firing stopped. There was banging on the door, and we heard the voice of Lieutenant Clark from 7 Platoon telling us to open up. The sight that met him must have been horrific: the floor of the 'Pig' was covered in blood from the wounded. All the casualties were quickly taken away by medics for immediate attention. All later recovered, but many bore scars to remind them of that day.

On returning to camp I felt completely exhausted. The whole action must have lasted for only 30 minutes or so, but if felt like hours. My shirt and denim trousers were completely saturated in blood.

I was only 18 years old but this experience had made me grow up fast. And in recognition of his bravery that day, 2nd Lieutenant Emson was awarded the Military Cross, which was well and truly deserved.

FIRST DAYS IN THE BUNDU

Belize is one of the few places where you can expect to put your training into practice. Although highly unlikely that you will find yourself involved in a shooting war, your tour is sure to be exciting in other ways.

When a unit is detached from 5 Airborne Brigade, it is still subject to recall. If necessary, another infantry regiment would then replace the Para battalion. This happened in 1982 when, with 2 Para's advance party already in Belize, the unit found that the venue had suddenly been changed to the South Atlantic and a group of islands that until then hardly anyone had ever heard of – the Falklands!

What, then, can you expect as a member of a parachute battalion in Belize? A typical tour lasts six months. First to arrive is the advance party, whose job it is to prepare for the arrival of the main body, finding out about tactical areas of responsibility (TAORs) and examining the departing unit's patrol reports. They also look at permanent OPs, areas worth observing and the type of information likely to be gained. By the time the main body arrives everything has been organised so that all that remains is for you to be shown your accommodation, after which you're left to settle in.

The next morning is spent taking over from the departing unit. One of the platoons is detailed with the first spell of camp duties, another with

One of your main tasks is to patrol the border to intercept drug smugglers bringing marijuana into the country for delivery to the USA. Travel by river is far easier than through the largely trackless tropical jungle.

Above: This river patrol is a joint venture between the Paras and Gurkha engineers. British forces have to do a good public relations job while in Belize, supplying medical aid to isolated villages.

carrying out local patrols and OP duties. Your platoon will be going straight into the jungle!

After taking over, you are given a detailed briefing concerning the platoon's tasks and area of operations; expected times for each task and what you hope to achieve; opening schedules for radios; pick-up time and grid reference and helicopter landing sites and pick-up points (PUPs) – including emergency landing sites and RVs.

Drug-trafficking deterrent

You're told that you are here for several reasons. Your presence on the ground acts as a deterrent against drug trafficking. Marijuana, grown in Belize by Guatemalans, still manages to find its way into the United States. Until recently it was your job to burn the fields, but this task is now the responsibility of local government troops. Your role is to patrol the border with Guatemala and to wait in ambush along smuggling routes and

apprehend suspected marijuana growers/smugglers. You are also to continue a successful 'hearts and minds' campaign amongst the locals – including administering medical aid if required.

Following the briefing, you are allowed a couple of hours to prepare your kit. You will be in the jungle for the next three weeks, and although there are those amongst you who have already visited Belize, there are others who have never even left Britain before!

Learning the hard way

The inexperienced listen to the advice of the older soldiers, but many will learn about jungle ops the hard way. Typically, some of you choose to carry excess kit – too much food and not enough water! You can afford to leave behind the extra socks and underwear you would normally pack, and you don't waste space with things such as boot cleaning kit. Experience will show that you can make do with just one spare shirt and denims, and *no* socks! If you load yourself down

At the jungle warfare school in Belize you learn some interesting new tricks. This animal trap is sprung by tripwire, releasing the sharpened stakes to whiplash against the prey. It is an old jungle trap, used by the Viet Cong against US forces.

The jungle warfare school instructs you in the full spectrum of military operations in a tropical environment with the emphasis on counter-insurgency. It makes a pretty picture, but in reality it is an unforgiving and hostile environment.

Paras undergo training in jungle survival and local skills. The instructor is a former Belizean Defence Force soldier. You have to make the bewildering variety of wildlife work for you.

At the start of the tour most of you carry too much kit, but you soon learn to operate with just one spare shirt, denims and no socks. Headbands aren't just to look like Robert de Niro: keeping sweat out of your eyes is important.

with 'luxuries' you simply won't be able to cover the required distance. Water is only readily available in the rainy season, so your main priorities are: water, medical kit, radio and spare batteries, ammunition and food – in that order.

Hacking a path

It doesn't take long to find that the 'bundu' is one of the most hostile environments you can find yourself in. Soon after leaving the relative comfort of the base camp, you are cutting a path through unbelievably dense vegetation.

With the lead scout hacking away for 15 minutes at a time before being relieved, progress is painfully slow. You stop and rest every half hour for half an hour, replacing lost body fluids with a hot brew. It is the dry season, and you have never sweated so much in your life! You are permanently wet through. What a place! You peer up at the canopy of foliage. Even the sun's rays fail to penetrate its density, so that everything takes on a gloomy green tinge. You wonder if you will ever see daylight again.

As for navigating, well, what a joke! The maps you have been issued consist of vast areas of closely packed contour lines (lots of hills) covered in green (lots of jungle). No roads, and very few tracks. There are rivers, or rather dry gullies, but how on earth are you supposed to tell one from the other?

At around 1730 hours you finally stop for the night. It is all you can do to put up your basha and cook scoff before changing into dry clothing and getting your head down. One thing to be thankful for is that you can hear anyone approaching when they are several hundred metres distant, so you can dispense with stagging on!

You lie beneath your poncho and listen to the jungle apparently coming to life around you. Crickets, beetles and other insects click and buzz. Just outside your basha, something scurries noisily in the undergrowth – a scorpion . . . a tarantula . . ?

Silent night

When you awake it is still pitch dark. What time is it? Just after two o'clock in the morning. Great! Still a few hours of kip left. You roll over and close your eyes, and suddenly realise what it was that must have disturbed your rest. It is deathly quiet. Absolute silence!

At around 0500 the jungle creatures again start up with their infernal din. You peer outside. Still dark. Close by, the hiss of a gas cooker indicates that someone else has had enough of trying to sleep and is fixing himself a brew. Good idea! You roll out from beneath your basha and wander across. Something crunches underfoot. A twig? Another horrendous insect? You decide not to check, and greet the bloke crouched over the cooker with a cheery "Good morning!"

The para looks up. In the flame's blue light his tired features look more haggard than they really are. "You're ****ing joking!" he replies with feeling.

Just two weeks and six days to go!

Join the Paras and see the world, eh? Having seen rather a lot of jungle in the last two weeks, this patrol takes a well-earned break. The mixture of M16s and SLRs is common in Belize, the M16 being handier in the vegetation and allowing you to carry much more ammo.